# Amateur Radio Explained

Ian Poole, G3YWX

Radio Society of Great Britain

Published by the Radio Society of Great Britain, Cranborne Road, Potters Bar, Herts EN6 3JE.

First published 2000

ISBN 1 872309 70 4

### Publisher's note

The opinions expressed in this book are those of the author and not necessarily those of the RSGB. While the information presented is believed to be correct, the author, the publisher and their agents cannot accept responsibility for consequences arising from any inaccuracies or omissions.

Cover design: Braden Threadgold Advertising.
Illustrations: Bob Ryan.
Typography: Ray Eckersley, Seven Stars Publishing, Marlow.
Production: Mike Dennison.

Printed in Great Britain by Black Bear Press, Cambridge.

# Contents

# Preface

It is some years now since I first started short-wave listening and then obtained my licence. Yet, despite the time I have been interested in amateur radio, I still find new areas of interest. I have also made many friends through the hobby. Some I talk to over the air while I meet others from time to time. It also gave me a good introduction to my career in electronics.

As you read this book, I hope that I am able to convey something of the fascination of the hobby, and the way in which it has interested me over the years. To this day I still remember the excitement of making my first contact, and then some months later the first contact, early in the morning, with the West Coast of the USA. Even now I find it fascinating that signals can travel over these vast distances.

In writing the book I must thank several people: Mike Dennison for his advice and suggestions, Peter Roberts for reading the text and making helpful suggestions, and my wife Pam who has tolerated me whilst I have been writing it.

*Ian Poole*
*Autumn 2000*

# CHAPTER 1

# An introduction to amateur radio

*In this chapter:*

- What amateur radio is all about
- Different aspects of the hobby
- Amateur radio as a hobby for life
- Transmitting licences
- How the hobby started
- The future of amateur radio

**An amateur radio station**

MATEUR radio is a unique and fascinating hobby that captivates the interest of millions of people around the world today. It encompasses a wide variety of subjects, from historical aspects right up to today's latest technology. It appeals to people of all ages, from the person in the street to politicians, kings and queens. While it is a technical hobby there is also plenty of human contact because it is all about communication. Radio amateurs, or *hams* as they are sometimes known, can make many friends through the hobby – some may be on the other side of town but others may be at the other side of the world.

## About the hobby

There are many areas of interest and activity that are encompassed within amateur radio. Some radio amateurs will enjoy certain activities whereas other people will get involved in different aspects. All of this brings a tremendous amount of variety into the hobby.

A home-built sta-
tion

For many years, one of the main attractions has been the possibility of hearing or contacting someone many thousands of miles away. In fact many people enjoy what is called *DXing* where they seek out stations far away or in interesting locations. Some people have stations with large antennas and sophisticated equipment with which they can regularly make contacts with stations on all continents. For those who may not want to spend as much there is no reason why they cannot take part in the action as well. With a little skill and cunning it is possible to make contact with people from many different areas of the globe with quite simple and inexpensive equipment. This makes it a hobby that is open to all.

Even though many people think of the short-wave bands as the place where radio hams can be found, this is not the full story. There are amateur bands on a variety of different frequencies. Several can be found on the short-wave bands, but there is also one just below the long-wave broadcast band, and others on the VHF and UHF bands and at higher frequencies. This adds further variety because the challenges of using the various frequencies are all different.

**A DXpedition**

Whilst operating equipment forms a large part of amateur radio, many people enjoy constructing their own. This is true even today when so much commercially made equipment is available. Although home-built equipment is usually much simpler than that produced commercially, it is still possible to use it to make interesting contacts, and there is an enormous sense of achievement when it works and the first contact is made.

There are other aspects. At certain times of the year the bands come alive when thousands of stations come on air to participate in some of the organised contests. They can be great fun to enter.

Also, some people enjoy operating from interesting locations. These expeditions, commonly known as *DXpeditions*, attract a great deal of interest on the bands and some may make many thousands of contacts in a few days. These expeditions are hard work but they can be most enjoyable.

Another part of amateur radio that has grown over the

years is collecting *QSL cards*. These are postcard-sized cards that are often exchanged to confirm a contact. They are normally very colourful, often having photographs of the country of origin and they provide an interesting record of the places that have been contacted.

**A QSL card from a DXpedition**

It is also possible to collect awards. These can be gained for a variety of operating challenges. One of the most famous is called *DXCC* and is gained for submitting proof of making contact with at least 100 countries. These awards provide challenges that add further interest to operating on the various amateur bands and the awards themselves are very attractive.

Computer technology is playing an increasingly important place in the hobby. Not only are there many amateur radio related computer programs that carry out important tasks like station logging, predicting radio propagation conditions and the like, but it is also possible to link a computer to the transmitter and receiver and communicate over radio using the computers. Early data communications used large, heavy teleprinters. Now computers are able to provide error-resilient systems with considerable degrees of flexibility to ensure amateur radio is truly in the computer age.

Amateur radio is also not just about enjoying yourself. In many areas it helps the community and on many occasions it has helped to save lives. It is an unfortunate fact of life that disasters strike from time to time, and often in these situations communications need to be set up swiftly, sometimes under very difficult conditions. Radio amateurs are uniquely placed to help at times like these. Having the equipment available, the knowledge required to set up a station, and the enthusiasm to help, they can provide a life-saving service. On many occasions amateur radio has provided the only means of communication from a hurricane-hit island because all the normal communications systems have been put out of action. In the UK as well radio amateurs provide significant levels of help and many groups using the banner *Raynet*® have been set up. Raynet® groups frequently run exercises to ensure a high state of readiness.

For those looking for a career, amateur radio can provide an excellent starting place. Many electronic development engineers started by having an interest in amateur radio. This stood them in good stead for further education. It is also a fact that many employers look for radio amateurs because they are known to have good practical experience in radio and electronics.

## Licences

Having listened on the amateur bands, many people will want to be able to transmit. The amateur radio licence allows many privileges and a great deal of flexibility. For example, radio amateurs are allowed to use high powers (very much higher than CB for example) and they are able to use equipment they have constructed or designed themselves.

As a result a degree of technical competence is required and so to gain an amateur radio licence it is necessary to pass some tests. These vary according to the country and type of licence required. All licences require the applicant to sit a theory examination, and some require a Morse test to be passed.

Whilst these may seem daunting to the newcomer, many millions of people have successfully managed to gain their licences, and a large proportion of them did not have a technical background.

## How it started

Amateur radio has been in existence since the very beginnings of radio itself. Maxwell, a great theoretician, postulated the existence of radio waves and then Heinrich Hertz was the first to knowingly demonstrate them. Later Marconi performed many experiments with these new 'Hertzian' waves, improving greatly the distances over which they could be detected. He believed they could be used for communicating over long distances and accordingly set up his own company. In his efforts to advertise his company he gave many lectures and talks as well as breaking new distance records. These captured the imagination of many people. Stories hit the newspapers, and this started a growing interest in the subject. Some hobby magazines at the time started to publish designs for making the equipment to study these new 'wireless' waves.

One person who heard a talk by Marconi was named M J C Dennis. His imagination was captured by the subject, and decided to set up his own station. This he did in 1898 at Woolwich Arsenal. He did not have a commercial interest in the subject and accordingly this was the first truly amateur radio station.

A number of other people followed in his footsteps as interest grew and more amateur experimental stations were set up. In these very early days no licences were required, but in the UK in 1904 the Wireless Telegraphy Act became law and people were required to obtain a licence before transmitting. Fortunately the act was interpreted favourably for amateur experimenters and the popularity of the hobby grew. However, it was not easy in these days. Very few ready-made components were available, and certainly no ready-made equipment. Interest continued to grow until the outbreak of the First World War when all licences were revoked in the UK and equipment was impounded.

After the war activity started again. This time amateur experimenters were soon relegated from the long wavelengths that were used at this time for long-distance communications. They were given the short-wave bands which were thought to be relatively unimportant. However, American stations soon reported making long-distance contacts and this raised the possibility of making a transatlantic contact on the short-wave bands.

After several attempts the first contact was made between a French station and one in New England and this was on a wavelength of around 100 metres (3MHz). Soon after this more contacts were made between Europe and North America, and shortly afterwards contact was made between a British station and one in New Zealand. Against all the odds radio amateurs had proved the worth of the short-wave bands.

**An early amateur radio station**

Technology improved in the 'twenties and 'thirties, and radio amateurs played a vital role in developing it and discovering more about the way in which radio waves travelled. However, in 1939 the Second World War broke out and activity ceased in most countries, including the UK. Nevertheless, radio amateurs played a key role and used their skills for the war effort.

Activity recommenced shortly after the war. The new UK licence had fewer restrictions than previously, and soon even more facilities were allowed. Shortly afterwards mobile operation and television were permitted and new frequency bands were allocated. These all gave rise to new challenges.

Again radio amateurs found their contributions were invaluable in many areas. Even so, people looked to amateur radio more as a relaxing pastime. More commercially made equipment became available, initially from the UK and the USA, but towards the end of the 'sixties sets from Japan started to appear on the market. Mobile operation increased with the greater use of the VHF and UHF bands and the wider availability of mobile and hand–held equipments for these frequencies.

Amateur radio operation from the Russian space station Mir

## The hobby today and tomorrow

Despite the enormous changes that have taken place in technology over the last few years there will always be a place for amateur radio. Indeed many of these new developments increase the interest in the hobby. Amateur satellites have been launched and there has also been operation from space missions, both American and Russian. In addition to this, new methods of data transmission have been devised that are far more efficient. Computer technology is being used even more widely. New forms of communication are being researched and devised, and computers are being used to act as digital signal processors where some of the functions of the radio are being undertaken by the computer. Computer technology in the form of the Internet is also having an impact on the hobby. Not only are there many amateur radio related web

An amateur radio satellite

**A data communi-
cations station**

sites, but it is also possible to access parts of the Internet via amateur radio transmissions.

For the future there will be many more exciting techno-logical developments that radio amateurs will use for their hobby. In the past the pioneering spirit of radio amateurs has paved the way. In the future there is no doubt that ama-teur radio will use new technology and in some areas it will help to discover or define new aspects of technology. It will always be great fun, and it is likely that there will be more variety in the way you can be involved and enjoy the hobby. It is certainly a pastime that will captivate you for life, pro-viding interest, friends and enjoyment.

# CHAPTER 2

# Types of transmission

*In this chapter:*

- Carriers and modulation
- Morse signals
- Amplitude modulation
- Single sideband
- Frequency modulation
- Data communications
- Television signals
- Simplex and duplex transmissions

**A**NYONE using a short-wave receiver will very quickly realise there are very many different types of transmission. Sometimes signals will be heard using the Morse code, while at other times voices or music may be heard or even a variety of different types of indecipherable sounds. All of these noises are being used to carry information of one kind or another. Some of it may be broadcast information, other may be short messages to and from ships, and others may be required to carry various forms of data, possibly even computer-style data. Even when transmissions are required to carry audio information there are a number of different ways in which this can be done. Some methods are better in some circumstances whereas other types are better in others.

## Carriers and modulation

A radio signal can be thought of as having two constituents. The first is called the *carrier* and this is the steady-state radio signal that is not carrying any information in the way of data, speech or whatever. It is simply the signal that is created by an oscillator circuit and transmitted or radiated. For it to carry useful information, *modulation* must be applied. This changes or modifies the signal in some way and there are a number of ways of doing this. Some are very simple but others used for some of the new forms of transmission like digital radio become very complicated. Fortunately those that are widely used in amateur radio are quite straightforward.

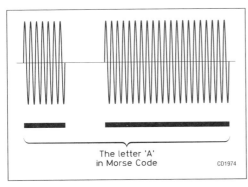

The letter 'A'
in Morse Code          CD1974

**Fig 2.1. A Morse signal**

## Morse

The simplest type of transmission is a Morse transmission. This simply consists of a carrier wave that is switched on and off to make the dots and dashes as shown in Fig 2.1. Although the Morse code was devised in the mid-nineteenth century and used for wire telegraph messages, it lent itself particularly well to being used over radio. In the early days, when technology was very basic, Morse was the only way of communicating via radio. Even when it became possible to modulate signals with speech or music, it was still widely used. Today it is only necessary to tune across the short-wave bands to hear that it is still being used extensively. The reason for this is simply that it has some advantages over other modes. The prime reason is that it is much easier to 'read' a Morse signal when it is very weak than any other type of transmission.

A further advantage that is particularly useful for radio amateurs is that the equipment is much simpler. It can be relatively easy to build a Morse transmitter, and indeed one can even be built using a single transistor.

The disadvantage of a Morse transmission is that in order to receive it a beat frequency oscillator (BFO) is required in many types of receiver. Without a BFO the incoming signal would sound like a series of thumps and clicks, whereas when one is used it enables the Morse signal to have the characteristic 'bleeping' tone. Receivers that are to be used for the short-wave bands usually have a BFO that can be switched in and out as appropriate.

## Amplitude modulation

The most obvious form of modulation is *amplitude modulation* (AM). Here the actual amplitude or size of

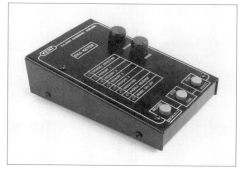

**A selection of Morse keys and keyers** *(courtesy R A Kent Engineering)*

13

Fig 2.2. Amplitude modulation of a carrier wave by a single sine-wave tone

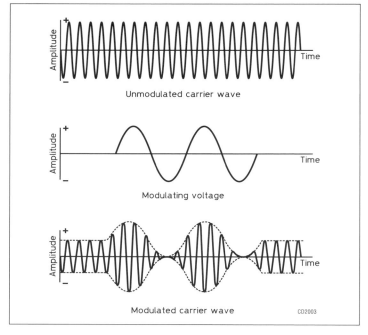

Fig 2.2. Amplitude modulation of a carrier wave by a single sine-wave tone

the signal is varied in line with the voltage of the modulating waveform. In other words, if the audio signal consists of a sine wave, then the radio frequency signal will vary in line with the audio signal as shown in Fig 2.2.

When a signal is modulated, *sidebands* are produced. If the modulating signal is a 1kHz tone then it is found that two other signals appear 1kHz either side of the main carrier. If the tone is replaced by speech or music that consists of a whole variety of different sounds at different frequencies, signals are seen either side of the carrier as shown in Fig 2.3.

Unfortunately amplitude modulation is not a very efficient method. It can be seen from the diagram that it takes up twice the bandwidth of the audio signal and it does not use the transmitted power very efficiently either. However, its advantage is that it is very easy to extract the audio from the signal in the receiver.

AM is mainly used for broadcast transmissions on the long-, medium- and short-wave bands, and also by aircraft above

108MHz. Other modes are used in preference by amateurs because they give better performance.

## Single sideband

Single sideband (SSB) is widely used on the short-wave bands by professionals and amateurs. It offers several advantages. It occupies less valuable space on the bands, and it also uses the transmitted power more efficiently. A single sideband signal is a derivative of amplitude modulation. As the carrier itself does not contribute to conveying the modulation, it is removed. Its actual purpose is to provide a reference signal for the demodulation process and it can be regenerated locally in the receiver. Also the two sidebands are virtually identical, the only difference being that one is a mirror image of the other. One of these can be removed to halve the amount of bandwidth that is taken up by the signal without any detrimental effects. This leaves only one sideband. If this is received on an ordinary broadcast set capable of receiving AM the signal will sound very garbled. To reconvert this back into intelligible audio a *beat frequency oscillator* (BFO) and mixer are required in the demodulation process. Often the mixer is called a *product detector* when used in this application, and the BFO may be called a *carrier insertion oscillator* (CIO).

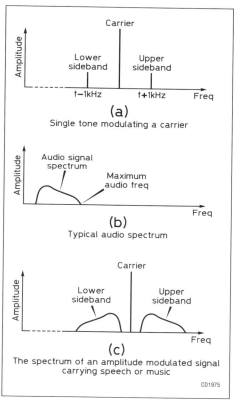

**(a)**
Single tone modulating a carrier

**(b)**
Typical audio spectrum

**(c)**
The spectrum of an amplitude modulated signal carrying speech or music

CD1975

**Fig 2.3. Spectrum of an amplitude-modulated signal**

As it is possible to use either sideband equally well, there is a convention for radio amateurs that the upper sideband (USB) is used on frequencies above 10MHz and the lower sideband (LSB) is used on frequencies below 10MHz.

When a single sideband signal is received the BFO must be switched on and its signal must be set to replace the carrier as shown. Any mismatch in frequency will cause the pitch of the reconstituted audio to change. A frequency offset of less than 100Hz is usually tolerable for most communications applications, and this can normally be achieved quite easily with a modern communications receiver.

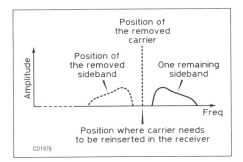

**Fig 2.4. Spectrum of a single sideband signal**

## Frequency modulation

Instead of varying the amplitude of a signal it is also possible to vary the frequency in line with the modulating signal. In some circumstances this has a number of advantages over amplitude modulation and as a result it is used to carry the high-quality broadcast transmissions on the VHF band. It is also used for point-to-point transmissions such as those used for taxi cabs and the like. Similarly radio amateurs use FM extensively on the VHF and UHF bands for mobile and other relatively local communications.

When frequency modulating a carrier, the incoming audio waveform is made to vary the frequency of the transmission as shown in Fig 2.5. In this way the amplitude of the transmission remains constant and only the frequency varies. When demodulating the signal to provide the audio in the receiver, the circuit must be frequency sensitive so that it changes the frequency variations back into voltage changes that can be passed into the audio amplifier and then into a loudspeaker or headphones. As it is only the frequency variations that carry the information, the levels of noise and interference that predominantly appear as amplitude variations can be ignored. Also fading and level changes have considerably less effect. This means that noise levels are reduced and

**Fig 2.4. Spectrum of a single sideband signal**

**Fig 2.5. Frequency modulation**

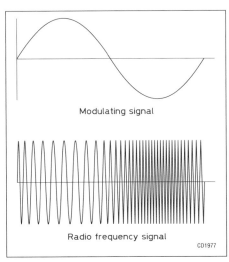

signal variations like those experienced in moving cars have considerably less effect.

The amount by which the frequency changes is called the *deviation*. This may be small, typically ±3kHz in the case of many point-to-point and amateur transmissions. This is known as *narrow-band FM* (NBFM) as it only occupies a relatively narrow bandwidth.

Broadcast transmissions have a comparatively large level of deviation, typically ±75kHz, and this is known as *wide-band FM*. Obviously, the larger the deviation, the wider the bandwidth the transmission occupies – these transmissions occupy about 200kHz but there are also improvements in quality.

# Radio teletype

Apart from sending messages via Morse or using audio, it is also possible to send data messages, usually text. The earliest type of data transmission was known as *radio teletype* (RTTY). Originally large, noisy mechanical machines, known as *teleprinters*, were required to print out or generate the data but today computers can do this job and are far more convenient and pleasant to use.

The data is modulated onto the carrier using a system known as *frequency shift keying* (FSK). This type of modulation involves changing the frequency of the carrier between two different frequencies. By using a beat frequency oscillator in the receiver the shift in the carrier frequency produces two audio tones. However, the receiver does need to be tuned relatively accurately so that the tones that are produced are within the requirements of the system.

When used with VHF or UHF transmissions (those on frequencies above 30MHz) a system known as *audio frequency shift keying* (AFSK) is employed. This type of modulation involves modulating the carrier (generally using FM) with an audio tone. This audio tone is then shifted between two frequencies.

Using this system the receiver tuning becomes far less critical and this is more suitable for use at frequencies in the VHF portion of the spectrum and above where receiver stability can be a significant problem.

## Packet

Radio teletype is an early form of data transmission which suffers from interference and transmits data slowly. With the rise of computer technology new forms of transmission are available. One of the most popular is known as *packet radio* and is found chiefly on the VHF and UHF bands.

As the name suggests, data is sent in 'packets' or short bursts and, once successfully received, the station with whom contact is being made sends back an acknowledgement to this effect. If an error is detected, a request to re-send the data packet will be made. In this way a complete message consisting of a number of packets of data can be sent and received without errors being displayed at the receiving end.

Apart from the ability to send messages with a negligible number of errors, packet offers many other advantages. A mailbox system similar to e-mail is employed. Messages can be sent to other radio amateurs but since radio is used there are no telephone charges.

In addition to this there is a bulletin board system. This is similar to the news groups on the World Wide Web where information is posted for people to access.

## AmTOR and PSK31

Although packet radio is the most widely used form of data communication on the VHF and UHF bands, other modes are preferred on the HF bands (below 30MHz). The reason for this is that the packets of data are relatively long and the much higher levels of interference and fading at HF mean that it is less successful.

As a result a mode known as *AmTOR* (Amateur Telex Over Radio) can be used instead. The way in which AmTOR works is somewhat different to packet. Groups of three letters are sent, and after each group the receiver checks to ensure it has received them correctly. If so it sends an acknowledgement to the transmitter which sends the next three letters. This mode is used when in contact with another station and is known as *mode A*.

When sending out general messages to several stations the method is changed slightly in what is known as *mode B*.

Letters are sent twice with a small interval between them in case any noise crackles are present.

Using digital signal processing (DSP) techniques on high-speed computers, it is possible to transmit and receive text messages almost error free on the very noisy HF bands. This method is called *PSK31* and software for use with a computer's sound card is available free on the Internet.

## Television (fast and slow scan)

The amateur radio licence allows the transmission of two types of television signals. The most obvious is the fast-scan system that is used for normal analogue broadcast transmissions. However, as this takes a lot of space (typically about 6MHz), it is normally only found on bands above 430MHz. The standards used for this are broadly the same as those used for broadcast transmission and this means that ordinary televisions can be used, greatly reducing the cost of any equipment that is bought and used.

The system operates by scanning an image. The light level at each point is detected and so a representation of the image can be transmitted. At the receiver a similar point is scanned and this reproduces the level of light at the transmitter. In this way a representation of the picture can be built up.

Obviously it is important that the transmitter and receiver are synchronised, and this is achieved using *synchronisation pulses* that are inserted at the beginning of each line and frame. This signal is then modulated onto a carrier.

For bands that are lower in frequency a system known as *slow-scan television* is used. This system uses up much less spectrum space or bandwidth. Naturally some of the advantages of the wide-band fast-scan television are lost, for instance the ability to transmit moving pictures. Even so it provides a very useful way of sending

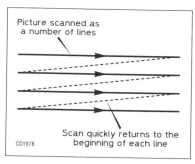

Picture scanned as a number of lines

Scan quickly returns to the beginning of each line

CD1978

**Fig 2.6. Scanning a picture**

**Fig 2.7. A television signal**

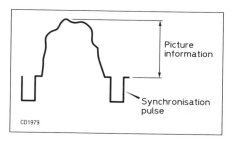

Picture information

Synchronisation pulse

CD1979

**Fig 2.8. Simplex and duplex op- eration**

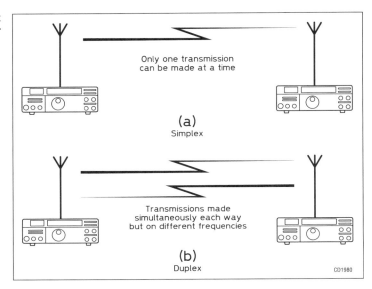

Only one transmission
can be made at a time

**(a)**
Simplex

Transmissions made
simultaneously each way
but on different frequencies

**(b)**
Duplex

CD1980

pictures around the world. The system operates in basically the same way as a fast-scan television system using a scanning system. However, the rate at which pictures are scanned is much slower and the number of lines is less. The normal standard for a picture is 120 or 128 lines a frame and may take around eight seconds to send. To transmit a slow-scan television signal the standard is to use an audio tone that is varied in pitch according to the light level. This is modulated onto a single sideband signal. An audio frequency of 1200Hz is used for a frame pulse, 1500Hz for black and up to 2300Hz for peak white.

## Simplex and duplex

A *simplex* transmission occurs when two stations are in contact and one is transmitting whilst the other is listening. Transmission has to be handed over from one station to the other, and communication is only possible in one direction at any moment. Simplex operation only requires the use of one frequency and is used by many point-to-point services like taxis. It is also the way in which radio amateurs communicate.

To create a more natural form of communication it is necessary to have communication in both directions at once.

This can only be achieved by having stations transmitting and receiving simultaneously. This type of system is known as a *duplex system*. Obviously the transmitter and receiver must be on different frequencies, and the separation must be such that the transmitter does not interfere with the receiver in the same station. Duplex operation is used for mobile telephones.

## Further information

- *Radio Communication Handbook*, 7th edn, Dick Biddulph and Chris Lorek (eds), RSGB, 1999.
- *Guide to VHF/UHF Amateur Radio*, Ian Poole, RSGB, 2000.
- *Basic Radio Principles and Technology*, Ian Poole, Newnes (imprint of Butterworth Heinemann).

# CHAPTER 3

# What you can hear

*In this chapter:*

- The variety of signals that can be heard
- The legal position
- Broadcast transmissions
- CB transmissions
- Amateur radio transmissions

**A**NYONE tuning the radio spectrum with a general-coverage receiver will be able to hear an enormous variety of signals. Some will carry sounds such as speech or music, whereas many others may appear as strange noises, and these can be carrying other forms of modulation that may be data, pictures, faxes and a whole variety of other transmissions. These may be coming from almost anywhere. On the short-wave (HF) bands they could be coming from locations in the same country, or they may be from the other side of the globe. On the VHF and UHF bands the distances the signals have travelled are likely to be much shorter, but even so the transmissions can be just as interesting.

## Legal position

Before we look at the transmissions that can be heard, it has to be mentioned that there are laws governing which ones are legal to receive. In the UK, the general rule is that it is legal to listen to transmissions that are transmitted for general reception. This includes broadcast transmissions (although a licence is required for television), standard frequency transmissions, radio amateurs and CB. It is not within the law to receive police messages, ship-to-shore transmissions, mobile telephone conversations and the like where reception is intended by a specific person.

## Types of transmission

The actual type of transmission depends to a certain extent on the frequencies being monitored. The short-wave bands naturally tend to carry a large amount of long-haul traffic. International broadcasting is one obvious type of transmission. Radio amateurs also make use of their allocations in these bands. Many seek contacts worldwide, although on other bands more local contacts can be made. Citizens Band transmissions may also be heard.

Apart from these there are many other signals around. News agencies often send out information, and some of these are general broadcast transmissions intended for reception by anyone. These normally contain propaganda information but nevertheless they can be very interesting. There is also a large amount of ship-to-shore transmissions. Again, special bands are set aside for these. However, with the growing number of ships equipped with satellite communications, the level of traffic on the short-wave bands is decreasing.

There is also a large number of other types of transmission. Some may be from embassies, some are military, some are general mobile transmissions, and there is a wide variety of other transmissions for different purposes and using different types of emission.

**Aircraft make widespread use of radio**

On the VHF and UHF bands there is the same variety of transmissions, but they are generally over a much shorter range. The most widely heard stations are the VHF FM broadcasts that are found around 100MHz, and also the UHF television transmissions. However, there are also radiotelephone systems, cellular telephones and many other point-to-point communications to be found on these frequencies. Aircraft use the frequencies just above the VHF FM broadcast band. These transmissions include those between the aircraft and control tower, and also many other short-range transmissions by people on the airport.

Apart from these there are many satellite signals. Meteorological satellites, communications satellites and also many communications occur for the manned space flights on these frequencies.

Radio amateurs also have allocations in this portion of the spectrum and they make good use of these frequencies.

## Broadcast bands

One fascinating aspect of short-wave listening is scanning the broadcast bands. By tuning around these bands it is possible to hear an enormous variety of different stations, even more than those audible on the medium-wave bands after dark. These broadcast in many languages, although it is

**A short-wave broadcast station antenna**

possible to hear a good number broadcasting in English. Not only is it possible to hear news from other countries, and from another point of view, but many stations broadcast interesting programmes about their own countries.

There are many different bands on which these stations can be heard. The long-wave band generally carries very-high-power stations that cover large areas. In the UK the BBC long-wave transmitter on 198kHz covers most of the UK, and there are many other equivalent stations within the areas of the world where the long-wave band is permitted as a broadcast band.

The medium-wave band is used for more regionalised broadcasting. Typically high-power stations may have a coverage area with a radius of a hundred miles or so. There are even a few international broadcast stations: the BBC World Service broadcasts from South East England on 648kHz and other countries also have international medium-wave stations.

The bands higher in frequency are used for true international broadcasting. Of these the 49 metre band is one of the busiest, with stations audible both day and night. Those at the high frequency end of the short-wave spectrum have less reliable propagation and stations may only be audible during the day and around the peak of the sunspot cycle.

However, during these times stations are likely to be audible from all over the world.

The VHF FM band is also interesting. Although stations are normally only audible over distances of a hundred kilometres, when there is a lift in conditions due to tropospheric propagation, or when propagation is supported by Sporadic E, then stations much further afield may be heard.

## CB

Citizens' Band radio is available in very many countries including the UK. The band that is almost universally used is to be found around 27MHz and operation is based around distinct channels. Dependent upon the country, operation is either freely available without the use of a licence, or a licence may be obtained with the minimum of formality. In the UK it is necessary to obtain a licence, and operation is on FM whilst some other countries also allow AM and SSB.

The idea of CB is very popular. Many people use it because it is a way of keeping in touch with friends from home or whilst on the move. Equipment is also reasonably cheap and easy to install, making it an ideal option for many people.

However, CB does not offer nearly as much as amateur radio. For example, there are far fewer bands, it is not possible to build your own equipment and distances are restricted. However, many people have entered amateur radio from CB and it can provide an introduction to radio. It is quite interesting to listen to CB transmissions, if nothing else to gain a feel for the hobby.

## Amateur radio

Throughout the radio spectrum there are frequency bands allocated to radio amateurs. Some are shared with other services but many are allocated only for the use of radio

### Table 3.1. Broadcast bands

| Frequency (MHz) | Wavelength (m) |
| --- | --- |
| 0.150–0.285 | Long wave |
| 0.5265–1.6065 | Medium wave |
| 2.300–2.495 | 120* |
| 3.200–3.400 | 90* |
| 3.900–4.000 | 75† |
| 4.750–5.060 | 60* |
| 5.950–6.200 | 49 |
| 7.100–7.300 | 41 |
| 9.500–9.990 | 31 |
| 11.650–12.050 | 25 |
| 13.600–13.800 | 22 |
| 15.100–15.600 | 19 |
| 17.550–17.900 | 16 |
| 21.450–21.850 | 13 |
| 25.670–26.100 | 11 |

* Tropical bands for use in tropical areas.
† Only allocated for broadcasting in Europe and Asia.

**Table 3.2. UK amateur allocations below 10GHz**

| Frequency (MHz) |
| --- |
| 0.1357–0.1378 |
| 1.810–2.000 |
| 3.500–3.800 |
| 7.000–7.100 |
| 10.100–10.150 |
| 14.000–14.350 |
| 18.068–18.168 |
| 21.000–21.450 |
| 24.890–24.990 |
| 28.000–29.700 |
| 50.00–52.00 |
| 70.00–70.50 |
| 144.0–146.0 |
| 430.0–440.0 |
| 1240–1325 |
| 2310–2450 |
| 3400–3475 |
| 5650–5680 |
| 5755–5765 |
| 5820–5850 |
| 10,000–10,125 |

amateurs, such is the importance given to the hobby by the international community.

The lowest band is found in the low-frequency portion of the spectrum between frequencies of 135.7 and 137.8kHz. The highest allocated to amateur radio is in the region of 250GHz, showing the vast range of frequencies available. It must be admitted that there is very little operation on the highest frequencies because they represent a significant technical challenge. Fortunately there are plenty of stations on many of the other bands, especially those in the short-wave portion of the spectrum, and those in the VHF and UHF areas. Particularly on the short-wave bands it is always possible to hear other stations. Even on the VHF and UHF bands where ranges are shorter there are large amounts of activity, especially at times when people are on the move and using equipment in their cars, or in the evenings and at weekends.

Listening to radio amateurs can be a fascinating hobby in its own right. An enormous variety of different signals can be heard. On some bands signals can be heard over distances of many thousands of miles, whereas on others different and interesting types of communication may be used. Sound, television and data are all transmitted and can be received when the correct equipment is used. This wide variety is one of the factors that makes the hobby so interesting.

## Further information

- *Short Wave Listening Guide*, Ian Poole, Newnes (imprint of Butterworth Heinemann).
- *RA169 Receive Only Radio, Scanners etc*, issued by the Radiocommunications Agency, available on the Internet at www.radio.gov.uk.
- *Amateur Radio Operating Manual*, 5th edn, Ray Eckersley (ed), RSGB, 2000.
- *Radio Today Ultimate Scanning Guide*, Richard Allport, RSGB.

# CHAPTER 4

# Jargon, codes and callsigns

*In this chapter:*

- Abbreviations and codes heard on the air
- The Morse code
- Signal reporting
- Callsigns and prefixes

**A**NYONE listening to radio amateurs talking over the air will quickly discover that there are a lot of codes and jargon or terminology that are used. This has arisen out of the necessity to communicate quickly and effectively. In fact many of the codes were originally devised for use with Morse. However, over the years they have been adopted for use in normal speech as well. Fortunately it is not difficult to learn these codes and terms. They are very useful, and also help to break down any language barriers. Although English is used predominantly on the amateur bands, the use of these abbreviations and codes helps those people who do not speak the language so well to communicate quite effectively.

## Abbreviations

Many of the abbreviations are quite obvious; some are technical, whereas others are not. An example of this is 'AM' for amplitude modulation. Others like 'ABT' are contractions of words (in this case 'about'), and came about because of the need to send fewer letters to speed the Morse transmissions. Not all of these are used in speech as they are not always applicable.

## The Q code

One of the commonly used codes is known as the *Q code*. It is used not only by radio amateurs but also by maritime and aeronautical stations. The complete code is very extensive and covers many aspects. Several of the codes are not of interest to radio amateurs but those that are of interest are listed in Table 4.2.

The code is designed for use either as a question or as an answer. For example "QSL?" means "Do you acknowledge receipt?", whereas when used as an answer "QSL" means that "I acknowledge receipt". In the table it can be seen that the question and answer forms are both given.

Often radio amateurs will be heard using these codes as part of ordinary speech because they are so convenient. For example, someone may heard saying "The QRM is bad" when they mean that there is a high level of man–made interference, or they may be heard talking about QSL cards – the cards used to confirm a contact.

## Table 4.1. Commonly used abbreviations

| | |
|---|---|
| ABT | about |
| AGN | again |
| AM | amplitude modulation |
| ANT | antenna |
| BCI | broadcast interference |
| BCNU | be seeing you |
| BFO | beat frequency oscillator |
| BK | break |
| B4 | before |
| CFM | confirm |
| CLD | called |
| CIO | carrier insertion oscillator |
| CONDX | conditions |
| CPI | copy |
| CQ | a general call |
| CU | see you |
| CUAGN | see you again |
| CUD | could |
| CW | carrier wave (often used to indicate a Morse signal) |
| DE | from |
| DX | long distance |
| ERE | here |
| ES | and |
| FB | fine business = good |
| FER | for |
| FM | frequency modulation |
| FONE | telephony |
| GA | good afternoon |
| GB | goodbye |
| GD | good |
| GE | good evening |
| GM | good morning |
| GN | goodnight |
| GND | ground |
| HBREW | home brew (home-built radio equipment) |
| HI | laughter |
| HPE | hope |
| HR | here |
| HV | have |
| HW | how |
| LID | poor operator |
| LW | long wire |
| MOD | modulation |
| ND | nothing doing |
| NW | now |
| OB | old boy |
| OM | old man |

*(continued overleaf)*

| Table 4.1. Commonly used abbreviations *(continued)* | |
|---|---|
| OP | operator |
| OT | old timer |
| PA | power amplifier |
| PSE | please |
| R | roger (OK) |
| RCVD | received |
| RX | receiver |
| RTTY | radio teletype |
| SA | say |
| SED | said |
| SIGS | signals |
| SRI | sorry |
| SSB | single sideband |
| STN | station |
| SWL | short wave listener |
| TKS | thanks |
| TNX | thanks |
| TU | thank you |
| TVI | television interference |
| TX | transmitter |
| U | you |
| UR | your, you are |
| VY | very |
| WID | with |
| WKD | worked |
| WUD | would |
| WX | weather |
| XMTR | transmitter |
| XTAL | crystal |
| XYL | wife |
| Z | GMT – the letter is added after the figures, ie 1600Z is 1600 hours GMT |
| YL | young lady |
| 73 | best regards |
| 88 | love and kisses |

# Morse code

The Morse code is probably the most famous of all the codes used for radio transmissions. It was originally devised in the middle of the 19th century by Samuel Morse for use with the old wire telegraph systems. With the introduction of radio it was found to be just as useful and it is still widely employed today because it has several advantages over other types of transmission as described in the chapter on types of transmission.

## Table 4.2. The Q code

| | |
|---|---|
| QRA | What is the name of your station? |
| | The name of my station is . . . |
| QRG | What is my frequency? |
| | Your exact frequency is . . . |
| QRL | Are you busy? |
| | I am busy. |
| QRM | Is there any (man made) interference? |
| | There is (man made) interference. |
| QRN | Is there any atmospheric noise? |
| | There is atmospheric noise. |
| QRO | Shall I increase my power? |
| | Increase power. |
| QRP | Shall I reduce power? |
| | Reduce power. |
| QRQ | Shall I send faster? |
| | Send faster. |
| QRS | Shall I send more slowly? |
| | Send more slowly. |
| QRT | Shall I stop sending? |
| | Stop sending. |
| QRU | Do you have any messages for me? |
| | I have nothing for you. |
| QRV | Are you ready to receive? |
| | I am ready. |
| QRZ | Who is calling me? |
| | You are being called by . . . |
| QSL | Can you acknowledge receipt? |
| | I acknowledge receipt. |
| QSP | Can you relay a message? |
| | I can relay a message. |
| QSY | Shall I change to another frequency? |
| | Change to another frequency. |
| QTH | What is your location? |
| | My location is . . . |
| QTR | What is the exact time? |
| | The exact time is . . . |

## Phonetic alphabet

When spelling out place names or when giving callsigns it is necessary to ensure that the letters are understood exactly. However, it is very easy to confuse those letters like 'b' and 'p' or 's' and 'f', especially when talking over the radio and when interference levels are high. To stop this happening a phonetic alphabet is used. People will be heard giving their callsigns out using this, for example "Golf three Yankee

## Table 4.3. The Morse code

| | | | | |
|---|---|---|---|---|
| A | • — | | N | — • |
| B | — • • • | | O | — — — |
| C | — • — • | | P | • — — • |
| D | — • • | | Q | — — • — |
| E | • | | R | • — • |
| F | • • — • | | S | • • • |
| G | — — • | | T | — |
| H | • • • • | | U | • • — |
| I | • • | | V | • • • — |
| J | • — — — | | W | • — — |
| K | — • — | | X | — • • — |
| L | • — • • | | Y | — • — — |
| M | — — | | Z | — — • • |
| 1 | • — — — — | | 6 | — • • • • |
| 2 | • • — — — | | 7 | — — • • • |
| 3 | • • • — — | | 8 | — — — • • |
| 4 | • • • • — | | 9 | — — — — • |
| 5 | • • • • • | | 0 | — — — — — |

**Punctuation**

| | |
|---|---|
| Full stop | • — • — • — |
| Comma | — — • • — — |
| Question mark (?) | • • — — • • |
| Equals sign (=) | — • • • — |
| Stroke (/) | — • • — • |
| Mistake | • • • • • • • • |

**Procedural characters**

Procedural characters made up of two letters are sent as a single letter with no break between them.

| | |
|---|---|
| Start of work (CT) | — • — • — |
| Invitation to transmit (KN) | — • — — • |
| End of work (VA) | • • • — • — |
| End of message (AR) | • — • — • |
| Invitation to transmit (K) | — • — |
| Invitation to a particular station to transmit (KN) | — • — — • |

Whisky X–ray" for G3YWX. The one most commonly used and adopted internationally by the International Telecommunications Union is given in Table 4.4, although occasionally people will be heard using different phonetics.

# RST code

When transmitting it is very useful to be able to receive signal reports. It helps to guide how to conduct the contact. If

**Table 4.4. The phonetic alphabet**

| | | | |
|---|---|---|---|
| A | Alpha | N | November |
| B | Bravo | O | Oscar |
| C | Charlie | P | Papa |
| D | Delta | Q | Quebec |
| E | Echo | R | Romeo |
| F | Foxtrot | S | Sierra |
| G | Golf | T | Tango |
| H | Hotel | U | Uniform |
| I | India | V | Victor |
| J | Juliet | W | Whisky |
| K | Kilo | X | X-ray |
| L | Lima | Y | Yankee |
| M | Mike | Z | Zulu |

strengths are low or interference levels are high then the contact can be kept short. Reports also help determine how well the station is working. If the reports are consistently poor then it may indicate a problem with the station. To give meaningful reports it is necessary to have a consistent reporting system.

The system that is universally accepted for radio amateurs is known as the *RST system*. This consists of three figures, one each for readability, strength and tone. Their meanings are defined in Table 4.5. The final figure for tone is only used for Morse signals. For example a voice transmission that is readable with a little difficulty and is moderately strong would be given the report of "4 and 7". A Morse signal that is totally readable, strong, and has a pure DC note would be given a report of 589.

Many receivers incorporate signal strength or 'S' meters and these can be very helpful when trying to judge the strength of a station. The meters are calibrated in 'S' units up to S9 and then beyond that they are calibrated in decibels over S9. However, it should be remembered that S meters are notoriously inaccurate and should only be used as a guide.

# Callsigns

Every licensed amateur radio transmitting station is issued with a callsign that it must use to identify itself over the air. They are very useful because it is possible to tell quite a bit

| Table 4.5. The RST code for reporting signal reception | |
|---|---|
| **Readability** | |
| 1 | Unreadable |
| 2 | Barely readable |
| 3 | Readable with difficulty |
| 4 | Readable with little difficulty |
| 5 | Totally readable |
| **Strength** | |
| 1 | Faint, barely perceptible |
| 2 | Very weak |
| 3 | Weak |
| 4 | Fair |
| 5 | Fairly good |
| 6 | Good |
| 7 | Moderately strong |
| 8 | Strong |
| 9 | Very strong |
| **Tone** | |
| 1 | Extremely rough note |
| 2 | Very rough note |
| 3 | Rough note |
| 4 | Fairly rough note |
| 5 | Note modulated with strong ripple |
| 6 | Modulated note |
| 7 | Near DC note but with smooth ripple |
| 8 | Good DC note with a trace of ripple |
| 9 | Pure DC note |

about the station from its callsign. In particular it is possible to identify the country where it is located.

All callsigns have a similar format, consisting of two parts: a *prefix* and a *suffix*. The prefix normally consists of up to three characters up to and including the last numeral. Either it may consist of one or two letters followed by a number, or a number, letter and then a final number (eg **GM3**XDV, **2E1**DBI). It is the prefixes that enable the location of the station to be determined. The remaining part of the callsign consists of up to three letters and these are the serial letters for the particular station. For example, in the callsign G3YWX, the prefix is G3 and the serial letters are YWX. In this instance the prefix shows the station is located in England. There are a growing number of exceptions to these rules. Usually they are special event stations, or DXpeditions to rare

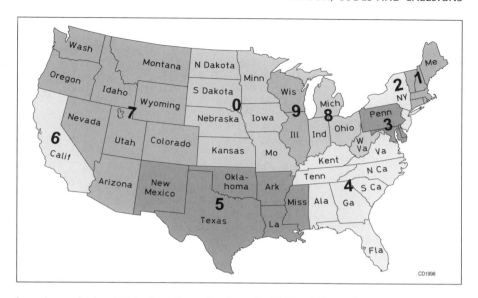

locations. A short list of prefixes is given in Table 4.6 on the following pages. A full list is given in the *RSGB Prefix Guide*.

**Fig 4.1. USA call areas**

Some countries are split into call areas, where different prefixes are allocated according to the area of that country in which the station is located. A prime example of this is the USA where the number in the prefix changes according to the call area as shown in Fig 4.1. Stations in California have a figure 6 in the callsign, eg W6, K6 etc. Those in the New England states have the figure 1, eg W1, K1 etc.

It should be noted that the call areas for the USA refer to the area where the call was issued. If the licensee moves state then he will not necessarily change his call, so some stations may be in different states to those inferred by the call number.

Occasionally additional letters may be added to the callsign. If a station is mobile, eg in a vehicle, it is normal to add the suffix '/M', and similarly for maritime mobile the letters '/MM' are used. Occasionally aeronautical mobile stations may be heard operating from an aircraft, and they use the suffix '/AM'. The suffix '/P' is used for portable stations. Other suffixes may be heard from time to time.

*(Continued on p41)*

## Table 4.6. Abbreviated callsign prefix list

| | |
|---|---|
| AA–AG | USA |
| AL7 | Alaska (and islands) |
| AP | Pakistan |
| BY | China |
| C3 | Andorra |
| CE | Chile |
| CN | Morocco |
| CP | Bolivia |
| CT | Portugal |
| CT3 | Madeira Is |
| CU | Azores |
| CX | Uruguay |
| DA–DH, DJ, DK, DL | Germany |
| DU | Phillipines |
| EA | Spain |
| EA6 | Balearic Is |
| EA8 | Canary Is |
| EI | Ireland |
| EK | Armenia |
| EL | Liberia |
| EM, EN, EO | Ukraine |
| EP | Iran |
| ER | Moldova |
| ES | Estonia |
| ET | Ethiopia |
| EU | Belarus |
| EX | Kyrghystan |
| EY | Tadjikistan |
| EZ | Turkmenistan |
| F | France |
| G | England |
| GB | UK special station |
| GC | Wales club station |
| GD | Isle of Man |
| GH | Jersey club station |
| GI | Northern Ireland |
| GJ | Jersey |
| GM | Scotland |
| GN | Northern Ireland club station |
| GP | Guernsey club station |
| GS | Scotland club station |
| GT | Isle of Man club station |
| GU | Guernsey |
| GW | Wales |
| GX | England club station |
| HA | Hungary |
| HB | Switzerland |
| HC | Equador |

## Table 4.6. Abbreviated callsign prefix list *(continued)*

| | |
|---|---|
| HH | Haiti |
| HI | Dominican Republic |
| HK | Columbia |
| HL | Korea |
| HP | Panama |
| HR | Honduras |
| HS | Thailand |
| HV | Vatican City |
| HZ | Saudi Arabia |
| I | Italy |
| IS0 | Sardinia |
| JA, JE–JS | Japan |
| JT | Mongolia |
| JY | Jordan |
| KA–KZ | USA (and islands) |
| KL7 | Alaska |
| LA | Norway |
| LU | Argentina |
| LX | Luxembourg |
| LY | Lithuania |
| LZ | Bulgaria |
| OA | Peru |
| OD | Lebanon |
| OE | Austria |
| OH | Finland |
| OK | Czech Republic |
| OM | Slovak Republic |
| ON | Belgium |
| OZ | Denmark |
| PA | Netherlands |
| PY | Brazil |
| PZ | Surinam |
| RA–RZ | Russia |
| S5 | Slovenia |
| SM | Sweden |
| SP | Poland |
| ST | Sudan |
| SU | Egypt |
| SV | Greece |
| T9 | Bosnia-Herzegovina |
| TA | Turkey |
| TF | Iceland |
| TG | Guatemala |
| TI | Costa Rica |
| TJ | Cameroon |
| TK | Corsica |
| TL | Central African Republic |
| TN | Congo |

## Table 4.6. Abbreviated callsign prefix list *(continued)*

| | |
|---|---|
| TR | Gabon |
| TT | Chad |
| TU | Cote d'Ivorie |
| TY | Benin |
| TZ | Mali |
| UA–UI | Russia |
| UK | Uzbekistan |
| UN | Kazakhstan |
| UR | Ukraine |
| VE | Canada |
| VK | Australia |
| VU | India |
| WA–WZ | USA (and Islands) |
| WL7 | Alaska |
| XE | Mexico |
| XT | Burkina Faso |
| XU | Cambodia |
| XW | Lao Peoples Democratic Republic |
| XZ | Myanmar (Burma) |
| YA | Afghanistan |
| YB | Indonesia |
| YI | Indonesia |
| YK | Syria |
| YL | Latvia |
| YN | Nicaragua |
| YO | Romania |
| YS | El Salvador |
| YU | Yugoslavia |
| YV | Venezuela · |
| Z2 | Zimbabwe |
| Z3 | Macedonia |
| ZA | Albania |
| ZB | Gibraltar |
| ZC | Cyprus (UK bases) |
| ZL | New Zealand |
| ZP | Paraguay |
| ZS | South Africa |
| 3A | Monaco |
| 3V | Tunisia |
| 3W | Vietnam |
| 4J | Azerbaijan |
| 4L | Georgia |
| 4S | Sri Lanka |
| 4U1ITU | United Nations Geneva |
| 4U1UN | United Nations New York |
| 4U1VIC | United Nations Vienna |
| 4W | Yemen |
| 4X, 4Z | Israel |

| Table 4.6. Abbreviated callsign prefix list *(continued)* | |
|---|---|
| 5A | Libya |
| 5B | Cyprus |
| 5H | Tanzania |
| 5N | Nigeria |
| 5T | Mauritania |
| 5U | Niger |
| 5X | Uganda |
| 5Z | Kenya |
| 6W | Senegal |
| 6Y | Jamaica |
| 7X | Algeria |
| 8P | Barbados |
| 9A | Croatia |
| 9G | Ghana |
| 9H | Malta |
| 9J | Zambia |
| 9K | Kuwait |
| 9L | Sierra Leone |
| 9M | Malaysia |
| 9N | Nepal |
| 9Q | Zaire |
| 9U | Burundi |
| 9V | Singapore |
| 9X | Rwanda |
| 9Y | Trinidad and Tobago |

With international travel being far more common these days, stations are often able to operate in other countries. When stations operate like this they generally use their home callsign with the prefix of the relevant country placed in front of it. For example, W8/G3YWX could be used when by an English station operating in a particular area of the USA. Occasionally the home call may be used with the prefix of the country in which the station is located added after the callsign as a suffix. However, this practice is less common these days.

# Further information

- *RSGB Prefix List* (updated frequently), RSGB.
- *Amateur Radio Operating Manual*, 5th edn, Ray Eckersley (ed), RSGB, 2000.
- *RSGB Yearbook*, Mike Dennison (ed), RSGB.

# CHAPTER 5

# Radio propagation

*In this chapter:*

- What radio waves are
- The radio spectrum
- How radio waves travel around the world
- How radio waves travel at VHF
- Other forms of radio signal propagation
- Using satellites

T HE WAY in which radio waves travel is a fascinating topic. Under some circumstances signals may only be heard over distances of a few miles whereas under other circumstances they may be audible at the other side of the world. Understanding how to use radio propagation conditions to their best is a skill that can be learned. Knowing when to listen and what frequencies to use can mean the difference between frequently being able to hear or contact stations from far afield, or just making the occasional long-distance contact. Those interested in making long-distance contacts spend time delving into the fascinating topic of radio propagation and using the conditions to their best. Even for those not interested in such contacts a good knowledge of the topic can be interesting and beneficial.

## Radio waves

Radio waves are basically the same as light or ultra-violet waves. The difference is that the wavelength (and hence frequency) are different. Fortunately it is not necessary to have an in-depth knowledge of them, but there are a few useful aspects worth understanding. In terms of theory it is more than sufficient to know that they consist of two components, namely an electric component and a magnetic component.

To gain a very basic idea of the way in which radio waves travel, a signal can be likened to a stone being dropped into a pond where the ripples spread out in all directions away from the centre point where the stone entered the water. As they spread out the waves reduce in height (amplitude), but cover a larger area. The same is true of radio waves where they become weaker as distances increase from the transmitter.

There are a number of points that can be noted about the waves. The first is that they have a distinct *wavelength*. This is the distance between a point on one wave and the same point on the next one. Normally the most convenient point to note is the crest or peak.

The wavelengths of radio waves are normally measured in metres. They vary over a wide range and may be many thousands of metres long, or they may be as short as a few millimetres. In years past the position of a station on the radio dial was measured in metres, and we still talk about the 'long-wave' broadcast band, the 'medium-wave' band and the 'short-wave' bands.

Another point that can be seen about the waves is that they vibrate at a certain frequency. Returning to the pond analogy, if the ripples pass a certain point in the pond, eg a stick in the water, then the water surface will be seen to go up and down several times as the waves pass. The rate at which the level 'vibrates' is known as the *frequency*. This is measured in hertz, ie cycles per second. These days the frequency of a signal is normally used to determine its position on a radio dial. Radio frequency signals are measured in many thousands, millions or even thousands of millions of hertz. Therefore frequencies measured in kilohertz (thousands of hertz), megahertz (millions of hertz), and gigahertz (thousand millions of hertz) are often seen.

As might be imagined there is a relationship between the frequency and wavelength. The longer the wavelength, the lower the frequency. They are linked by the velocity of the wave. For radio waves (and other electromagnetic waves) this is the speed of light. For most applications this can be taken to be 300,000,000 metres per second. If either the frequency or the wavelength is known then it is very easy to work out the other. There is a simple formula where multiplying the frequency and wavelength equals the speed of light.

$$\lambda \times f = c$$

where $\lambda$ (lambda) is the wavelength in metres (m); $f$ is the frequency in hertz (Hz); and $c$ is the speed of light (300,000,000 metres per second)

Take as an example a station broadcasting in the medium-wave band that has a signal on a frequency of 1 megahertz (1MHz). By inserting the right figures into the formula it can be seen that it has a wavelength of 300m.

## The radio spectrum

Radio signals exist over a vast range of frequencies. At the low end of the range transmissions exist on frequencies below

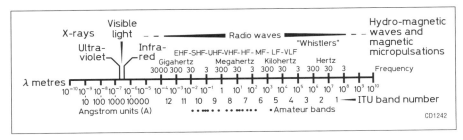

**Fig 5.1. The radio spectrum**

50kHz. At the other end of the spectrum transistors and other devices are being developed that operate at frequencies in excess of 100GHz. In order to clarify the radio spectrum it is split up into different areas as shown in Fig 5.1.Within these areas are contained all the familiar transmissions we hear each day. The medium-wave broadcast band is contained within the MF portion of the spectrum. The short-wave bands are generally located in the HF area. The VHF area contains a wide variety of transmissions including the VHF FM broadcast band and many point-to-point mobile communications. At UHF we find the analogue television transmissions, mobile phones and much more.

Within these areas there are many bands allocated to amateur radio. As they are spread over such a wide frequency range, this means that there is an enormous variation in the characteristics they offer. Some are able to support world-wide communications with reflections from the ionosphere, whilst others are used for local transmissions, and other frequencies are able to support communication via satellites. It is found that the way in which radio signals travel on different frequencies mean that some bands are able to support one type of transmission better than others, giving each band its own 'feel'. Selecting the best band for a given purpose means it is possible to make the best use of it.

## Radio propagation

The way in which radio waves travel around the world is dependent upon a number of things. In free space signals travel in straight lines, but when signals are transmitted around the Earth, they are influenced by several factors. The first is obviously the Earth itself. The areas of the atmosphere also have a major effect, different areas affecting different frequencies.

## Ground wave

Signals like those on the long- and medium-wave bands propagate primarily as *ground waves*. Here the signal spreads out away from the transmitter along the ground. It might normally be expected that it would only be heard over

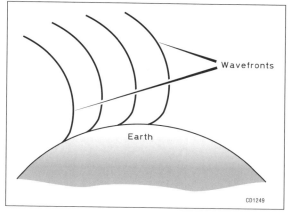

Fig 5.2. Ground wave

a distance equal to the line of sight because radio waves are basically the same as light. However, signals can be heard over much greater distances than these. High-power medium-wave stations can typically be heard over distances of 150km and more. The reason for this is that the signal interacts with the Earth and this slows that part of the wave closest to it. This results in the wave front being angled towards the Earth so that it can follow its curvature.

## The atmosphere

Before looking at the way in which signals propagate through the Earth's atmosphere it is necessary to take a brief look at it to discover something about its make-up. The atmosphere can be seen as a number of areas stretching from ground level right up to altitudes in excess of 500km as shown in Fig 5.3. Within some of these areas the radio signals can be bent and reflected so that they return to ground many miles away from where they were transmitted. It is found that some areas have a significant effect whilst others have very little or none. The two main areas that affect radio signals are the *ionosphere* and the *troposphere*. Each acts on signals in a different way, and broadly affect different areas of the radio spectrum.

## The ionosphere

It is the ionosphere that is responsible for worldwide communications on the short-wave bands. It is an area in the

**Fig 5.3. The atmosphere**

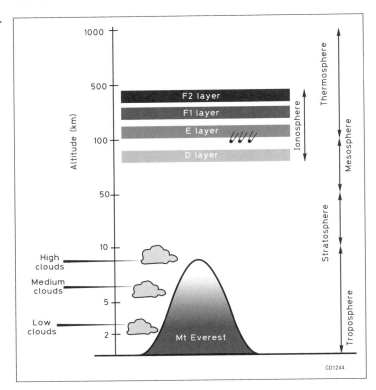

upper atmosphere where there are relatively high levels of ionisation.

This is caused because radiation from the Sun is so strong that when it strikes the gas molecules electrons are released, leaving *ions*. Whilst it is the ions that give their name to the ionosphere it is actually the electrons that affect the radio waves.

The ionosphere is often considered as a number of layers. In actual fact they are areas where the levels of electrons reach a peak, but nevertheless it is a convenient way to look at it.

There are three main layers in the ionosphere. These are imaginatively termed the 'D', 'E', and 'F' layers (see Fig 5.3).

The *D layer* is only present during the day and disappears after dark. It absorbs signals that are low in frequency. The

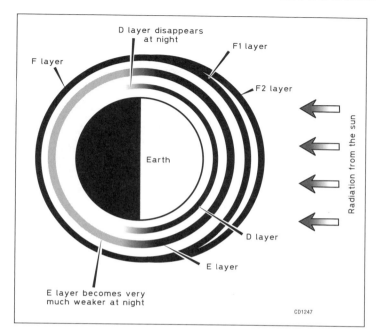

Fig 5.4. The layers in the ionosphere over the course of a day

results of this can be seen by the fact that medium-wave broadcast stations are only heard over relatively short distances during the day. At night when the layer disappears signals are able to reach the higher, reflecting layers and stations can be heard from much further afield.

The next layer up is known as the *E layer*. Like the D layer this is only present during the day, although a small amount of residual ionisation may remain overnight. This layer serves to reflect (or, more correctly, *refract*) radio signals. The degree to which this happens may be sufficient to reflect them back to the Earth.

Above the E layer there is a further layer known as the *F layer*. During the day this often splits into two layers known as *F1* and *F2*. At night when it is not exposed to the Sun's radiation, the level of ionisation falls and it normally forms a single layer.

It is this that is responsible for most of the very-long-distance communications on the short-wave bands. Like the E layer it also reflects radio signals.

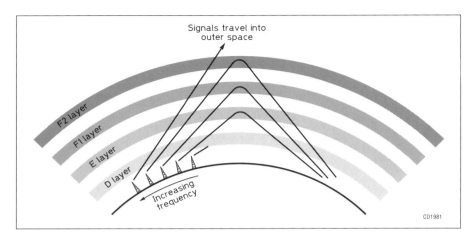

Signals travel into outer space

F2 layer

F1 layer

E layer

D layer

Increasing frequency

CD1981

## Reflection by the ionosphere

The way in which the ionosphere affects radio signals varies
with their frequency. To illustrate how this happens take the
example where a low-frequency signal is first transmitted.
This might be a signal in the medium-wave band. During
the day a ground wave will spread out from the transmitting
antenna. Some of the signal will also be transmitted upwards.
This is known as the *sky wave*. However, as the D layer will
be present during the day the sky wave is absorbed.

If the frequency is increased then the signal will start to
penetrate the D layer and it will reach the E layer. Here the
signal will be refracted so that it can be returned to the Earth
where it will be heard at some distance away from the transmitter. This will normally be further away than where the
ground wave can extend, and so the distances reached are
increased.

If the frequency is increased still further then the signal
will start to penetrate the E layer and it will eventually pass
straight through it, travelling onwards until it reaches the F1
layer. Here again it will be refracted back to the Earth, but
then as the frequency is increased still further it will pass on
to the F2 layer, being refracted back to the Earth.

Ultimately a frequency will be reached where the signal
will pass through all the layers so that it travels on into outer
space.

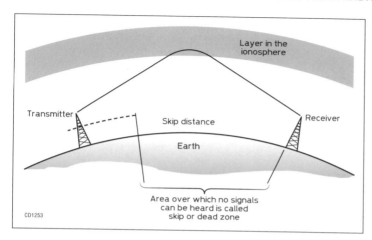

**Fig 5.6. Skip distance**

The other effect that is noticed is that as the frequency of the signal is increased the distance over which propagation by ground wave occurs decreases. This is one reason why short-wave broadcast stations are heard via the ground wave over short distances when compared to medium-wave stations, despite the fact that very high powers might be used.

## Skip distance

When a signal reaches the ionosphere and is refracted back to the Earth it will be heard over a wide area because the angle at which the signal reaches the ionosphere is quite wide. Even so there is normally a zone where the signal cannot be heard. This occurs in the area where the ground wave cannot be heard and before the sky wave returns to the Earth. This is known as the *skip zone,* and the distance from the transmitter to where the signal is heard is known as the *skip distance* (see Fig 5.6).

## Variations in the ionosphere

The state of the ionosphere is constantly changing. The time of day, season and the state of the Sun all play their part. At night when the ionosphere does not receive radiation from the Sun, the D layer disappears, the E layer nearly disappears and the level of ionisation in the F layer falls. The seasons also have an effect. In just the same way that the Earth receives

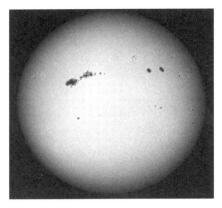

**The Sun, showing several sunspots**

less sunshine in winter, so the ionosphere receives less radiation. The state of the Sun also has a major effect. It is found that the level of the types of radiation that cause the ionisation is dependent upon the number of *sunspots*. These vary in number very roughly in line with a cycle that is about 11 years in length. Other changes on the Sun like flares can cause radio conditions to change drastically, giving problems with receiving short-wave band transmissions.

With all these variations, predicting the state of the ionosphere can be a bit like predicting the weather. However, after some listening on the bands it is possible to get a feel for the general pattern of radio conditions with the changes in time of day and the season.

The descriptions of some of the amateur bands in a later chapter give a more detailed view of the conditions that are likely to be expected. However, it is possible to give a very brief overview. Signals below about 2MHz travel primarily by ground wave during the day. At night, as the D layer disappears signals much further afield can be heard with distances of 2000km not being uncommon.

Signals above 2MHz and below about 10MHz can often be heard over distances of a few hundred to possibly 2000km during the day. At night distances again increase, and on some frequencies distances of 3000km may easily be achieved.

Above 10MHz the balance starts to change. Long-distance communications are also possible during the day, and those bands particularly at the high-frequency end of the short-wave spectrum may only support communication via the ionosphere during the day. On these bands signals may often be heard at remarkable strengths from great distances, even the other side of the globe. At these frequencies the effect of the season and the sunspot cycle have a marked effect. At the trough of the sunspot cycle ionospheric communications may only be possible on frequencies up to 20MHz or a little more. At the peak, frequencies of 50MHz and more may be used.

# Tropospheric propagation

The ionosphere is not the only region of the atmosphere that affects radio waves. The troposphere can also change the path over which they travel. The density of the air and the amount of water vapour that it contains change the refractive index of the air. As a result the index increases slightly towards the ground. It is found that light bends towards an area of higher refractive index, and this can be demonstrated by putting a stick into water and seeing the way in which the stick appears to be bent. Radio waves, particularly those above 30MHz, act in the same way, and under normal conditions it is found that the range of a VHF transmitter may be extended by at least a third beyond the horizon.

Tropospheric propagation of this nature primarily affects the VHF and UHF bands. It is not particularly apparent on the short wavebands, even when there is no propagation via the ionosphere.

Under certain conditions the change in refractive index of the air can be much greater and the degree of bending of the radio signals is accordingly much higher. This enables signals to be heard over much greater distances. Sometimes they may even be trapped in a *duct*. When this happens, VHF/UHF signals may be heard over distances of possibly 1500km.

When the propagation conditions are improved, talk may be heard on the bands of a *lift*. These improvements can be brought about in a number of ways. It is found that when an area of high pressure is present then there is a good likelihood of improved radio conditions.

## Other modes

There are many other modes of propagation that are available to the short-wave listener and radio amateur. These normally tend to be comparatively short lived and often occur only when a particular set of conditions is present.

*Sporadic E* is one such case. This occurs when small areas in the E layer become very highly ionised. The reason for this is not fully understood and occurrences of it cannot be predicted. In temperate zones like the UK it is found to appear more in summer. The level of ionisation is very high

**Fig 5.7. Meteor scatter propagation**

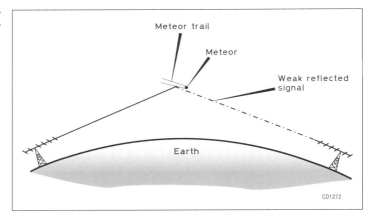

and frequencies as high as 150MHz can be refracted back to the Earth, although these openings may be very short, often only a few minutes. When sporadic E occurs the frequencies that are affected slowly rise, affecting amateur bands like 28MHz first, and higher frequencies later as the ionisation builds up. Having reached a peak, the level of ionisation falls slowly away. In periods of low sunspot activity sporadic E gives useful openings on the 28MHz band, and communications are often possible on the 50MHz band as well. It is also found that the geographical areas that are affected change during the course of an opening. The reason for this is that the area or cloud of ionisation is blown about by the winds in the upper atmosphere.

Another type of propagation used on the VHF bands is known as *meteor scatter*. This requires high power transmitters, sensitive receivers and effective antenna systems. All through the day the Earth's atmosphere is bombarded by small meteors. Also at certain times of the year meteor showers are experienced when the number of meteors rises very considerably. As the meteors enter the Earth's atmosphere they burn up, leaving a trail of ionisation behind them. This is sufficiently highly ionised to reflect radio signals up to frequencies of 150MHz and more. Although the ionisation only lasts for a very short time, possibly a second or so, this is sufficient to send some high-speed data, often in the form of very-high-speed Morse. In view of the unusual nature of

An aurora (Northern lights) can reflect radio signals

this form of propagation very specialised operating techniques are also required.

Another form of propagation that can be used on the VHF bands occurs when an *aurora* is present. Flares from the Sun throw out enormous quantities of material. When this reaches the Earth it can cause visible auroras to occur. These are known as the *Northern* (or *Southern*) *lights* and are spectacular to see. There is also an effect on radio signals. The normal ionospheric propagation can be disturbed on the short-wave bands but there are areas of intense ionisation extending out from the Earth's polar regions. By aiming the signals towards the areas of ionisation, they can be reflected back and heard over considerable distances. Signals that have been reflected in this way have a very distinctive 'rasping' tone because of the continually mobile nature of the ionisation. Also it is found that not all stations are able to take advantage of this type of propagation. This is dependent upon the size of the 'event' and how far the ionisation extends outwards from the poles. Often stations in Scotland will be able take advantage of a smaller aurora, whereas stations in southern England may not.

Another interesting mode of propagation is known as *moonbounce*. As the name implies, this type of propagation entails bouncing a signal off the surface of the Moon. In view of the enormous distances involved and the small amount of signal reflected back to the Earth, very high powers, very

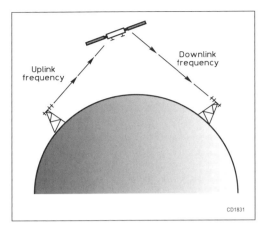

sensitive receivers and high-gain antennas are required. Many people use large 'dish' antennas to achieve the required results. Despite the many difficulties this mode of propagation, contacts can be made over enormous distances on the higher VHF frequencies and above.

**Fig 5.9. Communications using a satellite**

## Satellites

Yet another way of transmitting signals over great distances is to use a *satellite*. This technology is widely used by commercial users and whilst it may seem too expensive for amateur radio organisations to consider there are a number of amateur satellites in use. In general these use bands in the VHF and UHF regions, transmitting on one band and receiving on the other.

Most of the satellites are in what is termed a *low-earth orbit* (LEO). This means that the satellites move around the Earth unlike the much higher *geostationary* orbit where they remain in the same position relative to the Earth.

Using these satellites can be very interesting. It demonstrates yet another area where radio amateurs are using the latest technology in their hobby.

## Further information

- *Your Guide to Propagation*, Ian Poole, RSGB, 1998.
- *VHF/UHF Handbook*, Dick Biddulph (ed), RSGB, 1997.
- *Radio Communication Handbook*, 7th edn, Dick Biddulph and Chris Lorek (eds), RSGB, 1999.

# CHAPTER 6

# Bands and band plans

*In this chapter:*

- The different amateur band allocations
- Propagation and use of the bands
- Band plans – what each part of each band is used for
- Channels and channel designations

**A**MATEUR allocations are present in most areas of the radio spectrum. Each band has its own characteristics, resulting from a number of factors. These include the propagation, other users who may share the band, the equipment available, and several other factors. This means that for a particular type of contact one band may be better than another. Knowing what the bands are like and when best to use them is one of the operating skills that will quickly be learned. Knowing where to look for particular types of transmission is also vital.

In order to make the best use of the available spectrum, band plans have been introduced. These give a guide to the types of transmission that can be used in the different areas of the band. This helps reduce the levels of interference and makes the most efficient use of the spectrum.

## 135.7–137.8kHz

This band is the lowest-frequency amateur allocation and has only been available for radio amateurs in the past few years. With more countries releasing the band for amateur use the level of activity is beginning to rise.

In view of its place at the very low end of the frequency spectrum, it presents a unique challenge both in terms of operating and the technology that it used. Morse is generally used because it occupies very little bandwidth; several tens of Morse transmissions can be accomodated in this small band, whereas it is only wide enough for a single voice transmission. Many people use very slow Morse combined with exceedingly narrow filter bandwidths and digital signal processing techniques. Full-sized antennas for these frequencies would be very large so people use much smaller antennas. This presents new challenges for amateurs who use these frequencies.

Whilst activity levels are still low when compared to the very popular bands, interest is growing and operating on these frequencies is particularly rewarding.

## 1.81–2.00MHz ('topband')

This band is often used for relatively local communication. Being just above the medium-wave broadcast band it

| Table 6.1. UK 160m band plan | |
|---|---|
| **Frequency (MHz)** | **Allocation** |
| 1.81–1.838 | Morse |
| 1.838–1.842 | Digimodes and Morse |
| 1.842–2.000 | Phone |
| 1.843 | QRP (low power) |

possesses very similar characteristics. During the day distances of up to about 50km are possible, dependent upon the antennas in use. However, after dark when the D layer disappears the distances that can be achieved increase considerably, and stations from distances of over 1000km are often heard. It is possible for transatlantic contacts to be made, and at times it is even possible for stations at the other side of the globe to appear.

A challenge is to radiate a good signal from a small garden as a full-size antenna can be 80m long. The atmospheric noise levels are relatively high and this can make listening more difficult at times, but nevertheless gives the band its distinctive character.

The allocations for this band vary slightly from one country to the next. Many have full access to frequencies between 1.81 and 2.00MHz but some have restricted allocations. The band plan for the UK is given in Table 6.1. Note that 'Phone' means primarily SSB on the HF bands. 'Digimodes' are data transmissions.

## 3.50–3.80MHz (80m)

80m is a very popular band for local contacts. During the daytime contacts up to distances of 200 or 300km can be made relatively easily.

After dark, distances increase with the disappearance of the D layer. It is quite easy for stations at distances around 1500km to be heard, and stations from the other side of the Atlantic can frequently be heard. Transmissions from the other side of the globe can be received, especially around dusk and dawn during spring and autumn.

Interference levels can be high. Atmospheric noise is not as high as that on topband, but interference from other stations is higher because the band is shared by other services.

| Table 6.2. UK 80m band plan | |
| --- | --- |
| **Frequency (MHz)** | **Allocation** |
| 3.5–3.58 | Morse |
| 3.50–3.51 | Priority for intercontinental contacts |
| 3.50–3.60 | Preferred segment for contest contacts |
| 3.56 | QRP (low power) |
| 3.58–3.62 | Digimodes |
| 3.62–3.80 | Phone |
| 3.6–3.65 | Preferred segment for contest contacts |
| 3.69 | QRP (low power) |
| 3.70–3.80 | Preferred segment for contest contacts |
| 3.775–3.80 | Reserved for intercontinental contacts |

Nevertheless the band is popular and worth using as it can be very handy for short–haul contacts whilst still being able to provide the ability to hear or contact long-distance stations.

In Europe the allocation of 80m only extends to 3.8MHz. In North America the allocation extends to 4.0MHz. For the USA SSB or 'phone' operation is not permitted below 3.8MHz and accordingly split-frequency operation is required for two-way transatlantic phone contacts. The UK 80m band plan is shown in Table 6.2.

# 7.00–7.10MHz (40m)

Although small the 40m band is a very good hunting ground for people wanting to chase long-distance stations. During the day distances of 1000 to 2000km can be achieved but after dark these distances rise significantly. Transatlantic contacts are common and stations from all over the globe may be heard at different times.

Naturally the seasons affect the propagation conditions. In the summer it is usually necessary to wait until nightfall for long-distance stations to appear, although in the winter they may often be heard at almost any time.

Again the allocation available in North America is greater than in Europe, as it extends to 7.3MHz. This can make it difficult for those in Europe to hear North American phone stations because the frequencies between 7.1 and 7.3MHz are used by broadcast stations in Europe. The UK 40m band plan is shown in Table 6.3.

| Table 6.3. UK 40m band plan | |
|---|---|
| **Frequency (MHz)** | **Allocation** |
| 7.00–7.035 | Morse |
| 7.030 | QRP (low power) |
| 7.035–7.045 | Digimodes |
| 7.045–7.1 | Phone |

| Table 6.4. UK 30m band plan | |
|---|---|
| **Frequency (MHz)** | **Allocation** |
| 10.100–10.140 | Morse |
| 10.106 | QRP (low power) |
| 10.140–10.150 | Digimodes |

## 10.100–10.150MHz (30m)

This band was released after a World Administrative Radio Conference (WARC) held in 1979. It is allocated to radio amateurs on a secondary basis with other services having preference. Accordingly it has been agreed that only narrow-band modes including Morse and digimodes should be used. Similarly the band is not used for contests. However, 30m can be particularly interesting. Being slightly higher in frequency than 40m longer distances are possible during the day. Often it can be a good hunting ground because it is not as heavily used as many of the other more established bands. The UK 30m band plan is shown in Table 6.4.

## 14.00–14.35MHz (20m)

This is undoubtedly the major long-haul band for radio amateurs. Although it is affected by the time of day, season and the sunspot cycle, it is possible to hear long-distance stations at most times of the day, although it may close late at night. During the day stations up to distances of around 3000km away are generally heard, although it is by no means uncommon to hear stations much further afield at night. However, late at night few signals may be heard, especially during the winter and at the period around the sunspot minimum. Dusk and dawn also provide times when long-distance stations may be heard.

| Table 6.5. UK 20m band plan | |
| --- | --- |
| Frequency (MHz) | Allocation |
| 14.00–14.07 | Morse |
| 14.06 | QRP (low power) |
| 14.00–14.06 | Preferred segment for contest contacts |
| 14.07–14.099 | Digimodes |
| 14.099–14.101 | Beacons |
| 14.101–14.112 | Digimodes |
| 14.112–14.350 | Phone |
| 14.125–14.300 | Preferred segment for contest contacts |
| 14.23 | Slow scan television / fax |
| 14.285 | QRP (low power) |

In view of its popularity, the level of interference from other stations may be high. However, this does mean that there are plenty of stations on the band and there is always the possibility of hearing distant or interesting stations. The UK 20m band plan is shown in Table 6.5.

## 18.068–18.168MHz (17m)

This is another of the bands released for amateur use after the WARC in 1979. It is only 100kHz wide but, despite its small bandwidth, many people find that it is a worthwhile band capable of producing good results. The propagation conditions are fairly similar to those on 20m although, being higher in frequency, the band conditions tend to be a little better in the day and it closes earlier at night. It is also affected more by the position in the sunspot cycle. The UK 17m band plan is shown in Table 6.6.

## 21.00–21.45MHz (15m)

This is a very popular band. Being higher than 20m it is affected more by the state of the Sun, and is more variable. Often it will close at night and during the periods of the sunspot minimum no amateur stations may be audible. However, the signal strengths of long-distance stations are generally a little higher than those on 20m. To gain a quick view of whether the band might be open it is possible to listen to the broadcast band that starts right at the top end of the amateur band. If signals can be heard here then there is a good possibility that amateur signals may be present.

**Table 6.6. UK 17m band plan**

| Frequency (MHz) | Allocation |
|---|---|
| 18.068–18.100 | Morse |
| 18.100–18.109 | Digimodes |
| 18.109–18.111 | Beacons |
| 18.111–18.168 | Phone |

**Table 6.7. UK 15m band plan**

| Frequency (MHz) | Allocation |
|---|---|
| 21.00–21.080 | Morse |
| 21.060 | QRP (low power) |
| 21.080–21.120 | Digimodes |
| 21.120–21.149 | Morse |
| 21.149–21.151 | Beacons only |
| 21.151–21.450 | Phone |
| 21.285 | QRP (low power) |
| 21.340 | SSTV / fax |

The band is wider than any lower-frequency allocations. This can be a distinct advantage at times of high activity, and especially during contests. The UK 15m band plan is shown in Table 6.7.

# 24.89–24.99MHz (12m)

12m is another band released after the WARC in 1979. It is relatively narrow, but nevertheless it can be a good band when the propagation conditions are good. However, being relatively high in frequency, the propagation conditions are very dependent upon the state of the Sun.

In periods of low sunspot activity the band may not open during the day and no signals may be audible. However, when conditions are good signals can be heard from far away at good strengths. It is a good hunting ground for those people with low-power stations or antennas that are not particularly high.

Being high in frequency also means that it is generally a daytime band. Signals fall away in strength after dark, and in the morning it takes a while for the level of ionisation to build up and for many long distance signals to emerge. The UK 12m band plan is shown in Table 6.8.

| Table 6.8. UK 12m band plan | |
|---|---|
| **Frequency (MHz)** | **Allocation** |
| 24.890–24.920 | Morse |
| 24.920–24.929 | Digimodes |
| 24.929–24.931 | Beacons |
| 24.931–24.990 | Phone |

| Table 6.9. UK 10m band plan | |
|---|---|
| **Frequency (MHz)** | **Allocation** |
| 28.00–28.050 | Morse |
| 28.050–28.150 | Digimodes and Morse |
| 28.060 | QRP (low power) |
| 28.150–28.199 | Morse |
| 28.199–28.201 | Beacons |
| 28.201–29.200 | Phone |
| 28.360 | QRP (low power) |
| 28.680 | SSTV / fax |
| 29.200–29.300 | Packet radio |
| 29.300–29.550 | Satellite downlink |
| 29.550–29.700 | Phone (primarily FM) |

# 28.00–29.70MHz (10m)

This is the highest in frequency of the true short-wave or HF bands. It is situated just below the upper limit of the HF portion of the spectrum. The band is renowned for being very good when it is open, but extremely dependent upon the state of the Sun. During the low part of the sunspot cycle very few signals are heard, but as the sunspot numbers start to rise, so the conditions on the band improve.

Like 12m it is essentially a daytime band, but at the peak of the sunspot cycle it may remain open after dark. When the band is open signals from all over the world can be heard at very good strengths, and those with moderate stations can easily make many good contacts. During the low part of the sunspot cycle, sporadic E is experienced and gives the possibility of some long-distance contacts. Being very wide (1.7MHz), the levels of interference are generally lower. The bandwidth also gives the opportunity to use other types of transmission. At the high-frequency end of the band, FM operation takes place and there are even some repeaters. In

| Table 6.10. UK 6m band plan | |
|---|---|
| **Frequency (MHz)** | **Allocation** |
| 50.000–50.100 | Morse |
| 50.020–50.080 | Beacons |
| 50.090 | Morse calling frequency |
| 50.100–50.500 | SSB and Morse |
| 50.100–50.130 | DX window |
| 50.110 | Intercontinental calling frequency |
| 50.150 | SSB centre of activity |
| 50.185 | Cross-band centre of activity |
| 50.500–51.830 | All modes |
| 50.500–50.700 | Digital communications |
| 50.510 | Slow scan television |
| 50.550 | Fax |
| 50.600 | RTTY (Radio teletype) |
| 50.710–50.910 | FM repeater outputs |
| 51.120 | Emergency communications priority |
| 51.210–51.410 | FM Repeater inputs |
| 51.430–51.590 | FM telephony |
| 51.510 | FM calling frequency |
| 51.940–52.000 | Emergency communications priority |

addition to this a section of the band is reserved for satellite operation. All of these aspects make 10m very interesting both in terms of the propagation that can be experienced and the variety of ways in which communication can be established. The UK 10m band plan is shown in Table 6.9.

## 50–52MHz (6m)

This is the lowest of the VHF bands, being very close in frequency to the HF portion of the spectrum. At the peak of the sunspot cycle worldwide communication is possible, with long-distance stations being heard at very good strength. However, at either side of the peak when the ionosphere does not support propagation at these frequencies, distances are normally much shorter and the band takes on a feel more akin to that of the other VHF bands. Even under these conditions sporadic E gives the possibility of long-distance contacts. The UK 6m band plan is shown in Table 6.10.

## 70.0–70.5MHz (4m)

This band of frequencies is only available for amateur operation in a very limited number of countries of which the UK is

| Table 6.11. UK 4m band plan | |
|---|---|
| **Frequency (MHz)** | **Allocation** |
| 70.000–70.030 | Beacons |
| 70.030 | Personal beacons |
| 70.030–70.250 | SSB and Morse only |
| 70.150 | Meteor scatter calling |
| 70.185 | Cross-band activity centre |
| 70.200 | SSB / Morse calling frequency |

one. However, it has been recognised that an amateur band on this frequency would be of great benefit to the amateur community and there is a possibility that in the future this allocation might be more widespread.

Since there are very few countries active on the band there is little commercial equipment available, and this results in most of the equipment being either home built or ex-mobile radio equipment (from taxis etc) that has been modified for the band. This makes 4m very interesting and appealing to many.

Propagation is very much like that found on 50MHz although normal ionospheric propagation is rarely experienced. Sporadic E does produce some excellent results when it appears, although contacts with other countries often have to be on a cross-band basis, with stations from outside the UK transmitting on either 50MHz or 28MHz. The UK 4m band plan is shown in Table 6.11.

## 144–146MHz (2m)

This is the most popular of the VHF and UHF bands, especially where FM local and mobile operation is concerned. There is a comprehensive set of 2m repeaters that together cover large parts of the UK. There is also a large level of data (packet radio) activity. For those interested in long-distance contacts there is also SSB and Morse activity which rises significantly during contests or when propagation conditions are good.

The ranges that can be achieved often depend very largely on the antenna, transmitter power and location. However, for most stations distances of at least 30 to 50km should be possible.

| Table 6.12. UK 2m band plan | |
|---|---|
| **Frequency (MHz)** | **Allocation** |
| 144.000–144.035 | Moonbounce (EME) operation – Morse and SSB |
| 144.035–144.150 | Morse |
| 144.050 | Morse calling frequency |
| 144.150–144.400 | SSB and Morse |
| 144.300 | SSB calling frequency |
| 144.400–144.490 | Beacons |
| 144.490–144.500 | All modes (non-channelised) |
| 144.500 | SSTV calling frequency |
| 144.600 | RTTY calling frequency |
| 144.625–144.675 | Emergency communications priority |
| 144.700 | Fax calling frequency |
| 144.775–144.800 | Emergency communications priority |
| 144.800–144.990 | Digital modes |
| 144.990–145.000 | Guard band |
| 145.000–145.200 | FM repeater inputs |
| 145.200–145.600 | FM Simplex channels |
| 145.600–145.800 | FM repeater outputs |
| 145.800–146.000 | Satellites |

Those with high powers, good antennas and a good location will be able to reach much greater distances, especially when using SSB or Morse. When conditions on the band improve as a result of tropospheric propagation distances up to 1000km can be reached on occasions, and with sporadic E it is possible to make contacts over distances of some 2000km. However, this is the highest frequency amateur band where sporadic E can be experienced. The UK 2m band plan is shown in Table 6.12.

Operation on FM is *channelised*. This makes it much easier to locate a particular frequency, especially when operating mobile. It also reduces the level of interference because channels are spaced such that a station on one channel does not interfere with one on the next. Channels are identified by letters and numbers as shown in Table 6.13 overleaf. A system of channels spaced by 12.5kHz is replacing the previous one where channels were spaced by 25kHz. The designations for the old channels are shown in brackets.

# 430–440MHz (70cm)

Like 2m this band is very popular for local and mobile communications. There is an excellent network of repeaters in

## Table 6.13. UK 2m FM channels

| Frequency (MHz) | Channel designation |
| --- | --- |
| **Repeater input channels** | |
| 145.000 | RV48 (R0) |
| 145.0125 | RV49 |
| 145.025 | RV50 (R1) |
| 145.0375 | RV51 |
| 145.050 | RV52 (R2) |
| 145.0625 | RV53 |
| 145.075 | RV54 (R3) |
| 145.0875 | RV55 |
| 145.100 | RV56 (R4) |
| 145.1125 | RV57 |
| 145.125 | RV58 (R5) |
| 145.1375 | RV59 |
| 145.150 | RV60 (R6) |
| 145.1625 | RV61 |
| 145.175 | RV62 (R7) |
| **Simplex channels** | |
| 145.200 | V16 (S8) |
| 145.2125 | V17 |
| 145.225 | V18 (S9) |
| 145.2375 | V19 |
| 145.250 | V20 (S10) |
| 145.2625 | V21 |
| 145.275 | V22 (S11) |
| 145.2875 | V23 |
| 145.300 | V24 (S12) |
| 145.3125 | V25 |
| 145.325 | V26 (S13) |
| 145.3375 | V27 |
| 145.350 | V28 (S14) |
| 145.3625 | V28 |
| 145.375 | V30 (S15) |
| 145.3875 | V31 |
| 145.400 | V32 (S16) |
| 145.4125 | V33 |
| 145.425 | V34 (S17) |
| 145.4375 | V35 |
| 145.450 | V36 (S18) |
| 145.4625 | V37 |
| 145.475 | V38 (S19) |
| 145.4875 | V39 |
| 145.500 | V40 (S20) Calling channel |
| 145.5125 | V41 |
| 145.525 | V42 (S21) |
| 145.5375 | V43 |
| 145.550 | V44 (S22) |

## Table 6.13. UK 2m FM channels *(continued)*

| Frequency (MHz) | Channel designation |
|---|---|
| 145.5625 | V45 |
| 145.575 | V46 (S23) |
| 145.5875 | V47 |
| **Repeater output channels** | |
| 145.600 | RV48 (R0) |
| 145.6125 | RV49 |
| 145.625 | RV50 (R1) |
| 145.6375 | RV51 |
| 145.650 | RV52 (R2) |
| 145.6625 | RV53 |
| 145.675 | RV54 (R3) |
| 145.6875 | RV55 |
| 145.700 | RV56 (R4) |
| 145.7125 | RV57 |
| 145.725 | RV58 (R5) |
| 145.7375 | RV59 |
| 145.750 | RV60 (R6) |
| 145.7625 | RV61 |
| 145.775 | RV62 (R7) |
| 145.7875 | RV63 |

the UK and many other countries, enabling a good variety of contacts to be made even when only hand-held or mobile equipment is available.

Contacts can be made at distances of 30km and more with an average fixed station, and more if good antennas are used. For those wanting to make longer-distance contacts, SSB and Morse are better than FM. Although activity levels on these modes are often low, they increase dramatically during contests or when conditions are good.

Tropospheric propagation is the most commonly used way in which long-distance contacts are made, although other techniques including satellites and moonbounce can be tried. However, moonbounce is really a specialised technique.

The band plan for 70cm (Table 6.14) is somewhat more complicated than some of the lower-frequency bands, and this represents the diversity of use. There are also differences across Europe, and some of these differences need to be accommodated within the band plans.

Like 2m, 70cm has a large amount of FM operation for

| Table 6.14. UK 70cm band plan | |
|---|---|
| **Frequency (MHz)** | **Allocation** |
| 430.000–430.810 | All modes |
| 430.810–431.000 | Low power repeater input |
| 431.000–432.000 | All modes |
| 430.990–431.900 | Digital communications |
| 432.000–432.150 | CW only |
| 432.000–432.025 | Moonbounce (EME) |
| 432.050 | CW centre of activity |
| 432.150–432.500 | SSB and CW only |
| 432.200 | SSB centre of activity |
| 432.350 | Microwave talkback calling frequency (Europe) |
| 432.500–432.800 | All modes non-channelised |
| 432.50 | SSTV activity centre |
| 432.50–432.60 | IARU Region 1 linear transponder outputs |
| 432.60 | RTTY (FSK) activity centre |
| 432.60–432.80 | IARU Region 1 linear transponder inputs |
| 432.625, 432.650, 432.675 | Packet radio |
| 432.70 | Fax activity centre |
| 432.800–433.000 | Beacons |
| 433.000–433.400 | FM repeater outputs (UK only) |
| 433.400–434.600 | FM simplex channels |
| 433.50 | FM calling channel |
| 433.55 | Recommended channel for rally and exhibition talk-in |
| 433.625, 433.650, 433.675 | Packet radio |
| 434.600–435.000 | FM repeater inputs (UK only) |
| 435.000–438.000 | Satellites and fast scan TV |
| 438.000–438.425 | Fast scan TV |
| 438.425–438,575 | Low-power repeater outputs and fast-scan TV |
| 438.575–439.750 | Fast scan TV |
| 439.750–440.000 | Packet radio |

which channels are assigned. These have a similar method for assigning the channel designations (Table 6.15). Although operation is not currently migrating to a channel spacing of 12.5kHz, new designations are being introduced that can accommodate this spacing. Again, the old channel designations are shown in brackets.

## Beacons

The propagation conditions can change significantly over a short period of time. Whilst there are many computer

## Table 6.15. UK 70cm FM channels

| Frequency (MHz) | Channel designation |
| --- | --- |
| **Repeater output channels** | |
| 433.000 | RU240 (RB0) |
| 433.025 | RU242 (RB1) |
| 433.050 | RU244 (RB2) |
| 433.075 | RU246 (RB3) |
| 433.100 | RU248 (RB4) |
| 433.125 | RU250 (RB5) |
| 433.150 | RU252 (RB6) |
| 433.175 | RU254 (RB7) |
| 433.200 | RU256 (RB8) |
| 433.225 | RU258 (RB9) |
| 433.250 | RU260 (RB10) |
| 433.275 | RU262 (RB11) |
| 433.300 | RU264 (RB12) |
| 433.325 | RU266 (RB13) |
| 433.350 | RU268 (RB14) |
| 433.375 | RU270 (RB15) |
| **Simplex channels** | |
| 433.400 | U272 (SU16) |
| 433.425 | U274 (SU17) |
| 433.450 | U276 (SU18) |
| 433.475 | U278 (SU19) |
| 433.500 | U280 (SU20) Calling channel |
| 433.525 | U282 (SU21) |
| 433.550 | U284 (SU22) |
| 433.575 | U286 (SU23) |
| 433.600 | U288 (SU24) |
| **Repeater input channels** | |
| 434.600 | RU240 (RB0) |
| 434.625 | RU242 (RB1) |
| 434.650 | RU244 (RB2) |
| 434.675 | RU246 (RB3) |
| 434.700 | RU248 (RB4) |
| 434.725 | RU250 (RB5) |
| 434.750 | RU252 (RB6) |
| 434.775 | RU254 (RB7) |
| 434.800 | RU256 (RB8) |
| 434.825 | RU258 (RB9) |
| 434.850 | RU260 (RB10) |
| 434.875 | RU262 (RB11) |
| 434.900 | RU264 (RB12) |
| 434.925 | RU266 (RB13) |
| 434.950 | RU268 (RB14) |
| 434.975 | RU270 (RB15) |

programs that are able to predict what conditions may be like there is no substitute for actually listening to see which paths are open. One of the most reliable methods of achieving this is to have a beacon station transmitting all the time. On 10m and the VHF and UHF bands there are several stations that do just this. However, another international system has been set up and is active on a number of the HF bands including 10, 15 and 20m, and it is being extended to other bands. Here stations all around the world are co-ordinated and transmit one after the other. They identify themselves and then transmit on three decreasing power levels before passing on to the next station. This means that only one frequency has to be monitored to gain a very good appreciation of band conditions. These beacons can be found at the centre of the 2kHz wide beacon allocations on the HF bands.

## Further information

- *Your Guide to Propagation*, Ian Poole, RSGB, 1998.
- *Guide to VHF/UHF Amateur Radio*, Ian Poole, RSGB, 2000.
- *Amateur Radio Operating Manual*, 5th edn, Ray Eckersley (ed), RSGB, 2000.
- *RSGB Yearbook*, Mike Dennison (ed), RSGB (published annually).

# CHAPTER 7

# On the bands

*In this chapter:*

- How to conduct a contact
- How to operate through a repeater
- How to contact DX stations
- About the locator system
- How to collect QSL cards
- About operating awards
- About contests

**W**HEN listening on the bands it takes a short time to 'learn the ropes' of what goes on. Topics like finding out how contacts are made, how to make the best use of the time spent, knowing how to search out the more interesting stations, what contests are and how to participate in them, how to operate through repeaters and the like are all important and they form the basic operating skills any listener or transmitting amateur should know. They enable people to gain the most enjoyment out of the hobby and to use their equipment to the best, whether chasing stations at the other side of the world or having local chats across town.

## Listen, listen, listen

One of the most useful pieces of advice ever given to someone who had recently gained his licence was to "listen, listen and then listen some more" before transmitting. Even prior to gaining a transmitting licence, listening is very useful because it enables you to find out at first hand how to conduct a contact, use technology like repeaters and so forth. It helps refine and develop the skills that will be so useful when transmitting, and above all it can be fascinating to listen on the bands to find out what is going on.

There is a great temptation when you are able to transmit just to put out CQ calls and expect interesting stations to reply. By far the best way is to seek out those stations you want to contact by listening on the bands and then calling them. It requires a little more restraint but it is far more successful.

## Basic contacts

Many of the contacts that take place on the short-wave bands are what are termed *rubber stamp* contacts, consisting of the minimum amount of information. These are a good starting place for many people. Especially when starting out on the air it is useful to know what to say. Also for those people who do not speak English as their first language it is relatively easy to have a contact using a minimum vocabulary. However, many people like to talk about far more than is contained within the basic contact. Often technical discussions may be heard, or stations may be describing the part of the world where they live. Whilst some will want to have long contacts and discussions, it is important to know what the basic elements of a contact are.

On the HF bands a contact will often start off with a *CQ* or general call. A formula known as *three times three* is a good starting point. The letters 'CQ', meaning that you want to have a contact, are repeated three times, and then the callsign (usually in phonetics) is repeated three times. This whole procedure is repeated three times. In this way the call is kept to a reasonable length and anyone listening is able to gain the callsign and the fact that a contact is wanted. See the panel overleaf for an example of a typical phone contact.

Any station listening who wants a contact can then respond when invited to do so. He will normally give his callsign a couple of times using phonetics and then invite the other station to transmit.

If the first station hears the caller and responds, he will announce the callsigns and then normally wish him good day and then give a signal report. This is very useful. Not only does it tell the other station how he is being received and can give information about his station's performance but, if conditions are difficult, the contact can be tailored to meet the conditions. Once the report is given it is normal to give one's name and location. Then the callsigns will be given and transmission handed over.

The second station will follow a similar format, giving a report, his name and location. On the next transmission information about equipment in the station – the transmitter, receiver or transceiver and the antenna are often given. Details of the weather are also often mentioned. Again callsigns are given at the beginning and end of each transmission.

On the third transmission details about exchanging QSL cards may be given and then they may sign off.

Once a contact has finished it is perfectly permissible to call one of the stations. Normally the frequency 'belongs' to the person who called CQ on the frequency but, if the other station is called, he may ask to keep the frequency or move off to another one.

Giving callsigns at the beginning and end of each transmission may seem somewhat formal. This fulfils legal requirements to identify the station, but also serves to let the other

## A typical contact that might be made on the short-wave bands

Hello CQ CQ CQ, this is G3YWX, Golf three Yankee Whisky X-Ray, Golf three Yankee Whisky X-Ray, CQ CQ CQ, this is G3YWX, Golf three Yankee Whisky X-Ray, Golf three Yankee Whisky X-Ray, CQ CQ CQ, this is G3YWX, Golf three Yankee Whisky X-Ray, Golf three Yankee Whisky X-Ray, and G3YWX, Golf three Yankee Whisky X-Ray is standing by for a call.

G3YWX, Golf three Yankee Whisky X-Ray, this is G3XDV, Golf three X-Ray Delta Victor, Golf three X-Ray Delta Victor

G3XDV, this is G3YWX. Good morning old man and thank you for the call. Your report is 5 and 9, 5 and 9. My name is Ian, India Alpha November, Ian, and the location is Staines, Sierra Tango Alpha India November Echo Sierra. So how do you copy? G3XDV, this is G3YWX listening.

G3YWX here is G3XDV. Good morning Ian and thank you for the report. Your report is 5 and 9 as well. My name is Mike, Mexico India Kilo Echo, and I am located to the north of London, Lima Oscar November Delta Oscar November. So I'll pass it back to you and see how you copy. G3YWX, this is G3XDV passing transmission back to you.

G3XDV, this is G3YWX. Thank you very much for the report Mike, and it is good to talk to you for the first time. The equipment here is a small transceiver running about 50 watts and the antenna is a vertical. The weather here today is hot and sunny, about 23 degrees, although we did have a little rain earlier. So I wonder how you are copying? G3XDV, here is G3YWX.

G3YWX, this is G3XDV. Fine business Ian and your transmitter is doing a good job for you. I am running about 100 watts to a dipole at about 10 metres. The weather here is cold and wet, about 15 degrees, but it should improve. Back to you, G3YWX, from G3XDV.

G3XDV, here is G3YWX. Fine there Mike, and your equipment is also doing a good job for you. I would like to exchange QSL cards. I will send mine via the bureau and I look forward to receiving yours. I don't have a lot more to say so I will wish you 73s to you and yours, and look forward to the next QSO. G3XDV, here is G3YWX listening for your final.

G3YWX, this is G3XDV. Yes, OK there Ian. Thank you for the QSO. I'll certainly send a card via the bureau and look forward to receiving yours. Best 73 and I hope to have another contact with you further down the log. All the best. G3YWX, this is G3XDV signing.

73s Mike, G3YWX clear.

station know exactly what is happening and when he is expected to transmit. Using good operating technique is very

## A typical Morse contact

CQ CQ CQ, DE G3YWX G3YWX G3YWX CQ CQ CQ, DE G3YWX G3YWX G3YWX CQ CQ CQ, DE G3YWX G3YWX G3YWX AR K

G3YWX DE G3XDV G3XDV AR KN

G3XDV DE G3YWX GM OM ES TNX FER CALL UR RST 599 599 = NAME ERE IS IAN IAN ES QTH STAINES STAINES = SO HW CPI? AR G3XDV DE G3WX KN

G3YWX DE G3XDV FB OM ES TNX FER RPRT UR RST 599 599 = NAME IS MIKE MIKE ES QTH NR LONDON LONDON = SO HW? AR G3YWX DE G3XDV KN

G3XDV DE G3YWX FB MIKE ES TNX FER RPRT = TX ERE RNG 30 WATTS ES ANT VERT = WX FB SUNNY ES ABT 23 C = SO HW CPI? AR G3XDV DE G3YWX

G3YWX DE G3XDV R R AGN IAN = RIG ERE RNG 100 WATTS ES ANT DIPOLE UP 10 METRES = WX WET ES COLD ABT 15 C = G3YWX DE G3XDV KN

G3XDV DE G3YWX FB MIKE ES UR RIG DOING FB. ERE QRU = QSL VIA BURO = 73 ES HPE CUAGN SN AR G3XDV DE G3YWX KN

G3YWX DE G3XDV R R QRU ALSO = QSL FB VIA BURO = SO TNX FER QSO 73 ES BCNU AR G3YWX DE G3XDV VA

G3XDV DE G3YWX FM 73 ES BCNU AR G3XDV DE G3YWX VA

Note that the '=' sign is used as a full stop or break.

important and helps contact to be maintained with the minimum possibility of confusion, especially when conditions are poor or interference levels are high. In essence one of the keys to becoming a good operator is to let the other station know exactly what you are doing and not leave him guessing.

When a station in a very rare location is on the band or during contests, contacts are usually kept much shorter to enable as many contacts as possible to be made. Usually the contact will consist of just the callsigns of the stations and then a report. Speedy operating is of the essence under these conditions to ensure that others are not kept waiting.

When using Morse, similar contacts can be made. The main difference is that far more abbreviations are used to ensure that the speed at which information can be passed is as quick as possible. See the panel above for an example of a typical Morse contact.

Operation on the VHF and UHF bands using FM tends to be rather different. People are interested in longer contacts where they might talk about a wide variety of topics, technical or otherwise. A short call may be made on the calling channel to check if anyone is available for a contact. A full CQ call is rarely made, but instead a call of the form "G3YWX is listening on this channel for a contact", or possibly for a particular station. The channel is not occupied for any length of time in case others want to use the channel. Once a contact is made stations move off to another clear channel. Accordingly it is wise to check which channels might be free before making a call.

Again, callsigns should be used at the beginning an end of each transmission, although generally there is less emphasis on the use of the phonetic alphabet. Reports are exchanged and, if the stations have not made contact before, names and locations are given. The contacts are generally less formalised than they are on the HF bands because of the prevailing conditions and the fact that people generally want to talk for longer, and often know one another better.

## Repeaters

Repeaters are widely used on the VHF and UHF bands where they enable stations with poor antennas and locations (eg mobile or portable stations) to make contacts over much greater distances. The repeater generally has a very good location, giving it a wide coverage area. Stations are able to transmit into it and their transmissions are relayed on another frequency.

According to the band in use there is a set separation between the transmit and receive frequencies. This is 500kHz on the 50MHz band, 600kHz on 145MHz, 1.6MHz on 423MHz and 6MHz on 1.3GHz. The channel spacing is generally 25kHz except for the 50MHz band where it is only 10kHz and on 144MHz where it is 12.5kHz.

Repeaters have a number of automatically controlled functions. These enable them to operate in a more efficient manner. This means that when operating through a repeater it is essential to have a basic knowledge of its operation so that it can be used satisfactorily.

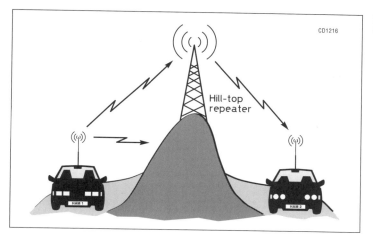

CD1216

**Fig 7.1. Operation though a repeater**

Hill-top repeater

Initially when a repeater is not in use it will not radiate a signal. To 'open' the repeater up there must be a signal on its receive or *input* frequency. This signal must be sufficiently strong for re-transmission and it must also have a tone to signify to the repeater that its transmission is to be re-radiated.

There are two methods of achieving this. The first is to use a *tone burst* at the beginning of the transmission. An alternative to this is a system known as *CTCSS* where a sub-audible tone is transmitted (see later). The use of a tone burst at the beginning of a transmission is the simplest way to access a repeater. It consists of a short tone (less than a second) at the beginning of the first transmission to open the repeater. The standard frequency adopted for this is 1750Hz. A margin of 25Hz either way will normally access a repeater although it is wise to maintain the tone burst frequency more accurately than this.

Once the repeater has been accessed, the incoming signal will be transmitted on the output frequency. Some repeaters have a *time-out* facility. This monitors the time a signal has been relayed and if a certain time has been exceeded the repeater will go into a *busy* or *time-out* mode and stop re-transmitting the signal. This generally occurs after about two minutes on 2m repeaters or five minutes on 70cm ones. This facility is included to discourage people from talking too long on the repeater.

| Table 7.1. CTCSS tones | |
|---|---|
| A | 67.1Hz |
| B | 71.9 |
| C | 77.0 |
| D | 82.5 |
| E | 88.5 |
| F | 94.8 |
| G | 103.5 |
| H | 110.9 |
| J | 118.8 |

When a transmission is complete the repeater will detect that the signal has disappeared from its input. After a short delay it will transmit an audio Morse character as an invitation for the next station to transmit. This character is often a 'K'. At this point the timers are reset and a new transmission can start. However, this time no tone burst is required.

Once a contact has been completed and there are no further transmissions appearing on its input the repeater will close down. Before any further transmission can be made it will have to be re-opened.

With the rise in the number of repeaters, channels have to be re-used relatively frequently. As a result it is sometimes possible for a station to access more than one repeater at any given time with the tone burst system described earlier. This is obviously not desirable and a system known as *CTCSS* (Continuous Tone Coded Squelch System) has been devised to overcome it.

Many UK 2m and 70cm repeaters are set up to use CTCSS tones. By careful planning of the network, it is not possible to access two repeaters with the same CTCSS tone on the same channel. Repeaters that use CTCSS tones transmit the letter corresponding to the tone when it transmits its callsign. This tone can then be programmed in to transceivers that have the CTCSS facility.

It should also be noted that repeaters using CTCSS can still be activated using a tone burst.

Activity on repeaters is often very high. This means that it is necessary to maintain high standards of operating and, in particular, not use the repeater for too long.

There are also a number of procedures that are special to repeater use. The first is to note that CQ calls are not made. Instead stations announce that they are "listening through" the repeater. This can be done quickly and it is quite sufficient to enable other stations to hear anyone who is calling and then to reply. When a contact has been set up it will follow very much the same format as any other contact at VHF or UHF. Reports of how the signal is being received into the repeater as well as names and locations will be exchanged. Once the

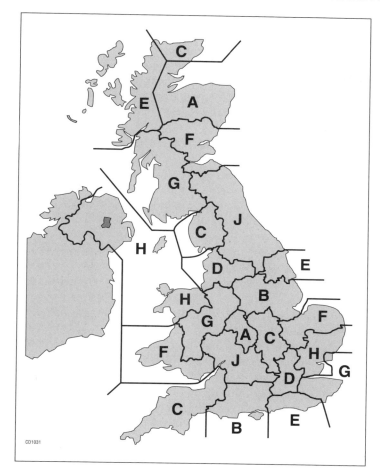

Fig 7.2. CTCSS tones in the UK were originally planned according to this map. There are now several exceptions, however

formalities are completed the conversation could be about virtually anything.

Once a contact has been set up it is quite possible that both stations find they can complete their contact without the use of the repeater. This is particularly true, for example, when two mobile stations are moving towards one another. If this is so then the repeater should be vacated to allow others to use it.

In addition to this, as repeaters are intended mainly for mobile stations, fixed stations should only use them when absolutely necessary and priority should be given to mobile stations.

Finally, even though all repeaters follow the same basic rules, they will vary slightly. Therefore it is always wise to listen to the repeater for a while before actually using it. If this is done few problems should be encountered.

## DXing techniques

Many people like chasing after far-off stations or those in rare locations. It can be a real challenge to make contact with a new country when many other people are calling at the same time. It requires operating skill to be able to find these stations in the first place, and then make contact against the competition.

The first stage in the process is to find the stations. There are plenty of aspects to this. The propagation conditions are obviously an important start. It is necessary to know what the conditions are like on any given band. This can be as-certained in a number of ways as discussed in Chapter 5. In addition to this it is well worth listening on the bands to get a feel for what the conditions are like.

Information about special stations also appears in radio magazines and on the Internet. This will give a good idea of what to look out for. Often times and frequencies where they have been heard before are given and these offer a guide to any favoured frequencies, times and where and when they may appear in the future.

There is also a lot of skill that can be gained to help home in quickly on any interesting stations on the band. Aspects such as the operator speaking with a different accent to the rest of the stations on the band, or sounding different in some way. Also when tuning up and down the band it is worth listening out for a 'pile-up' where many people are trying to call a particular station.

When calling someone in a pile-up it is necessary to get your call in at exactly the right time after the previous contact has finished.

Rapid and exact operating is the name of the game, giving your callsign quickly and accurately. However, in the excitement it is necessary to be careful not to call too soon or out of

place, thereby causing interference. Much can be
learned by listening carefully before making a call.

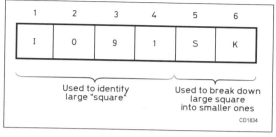

| 1 | 2 | 3 | 4 | 5 | 6 |
|---|---|---|---|---|---|
| I | 0 | 9 | 1 | S | K |

Used to identify large "square"

Used to break down large square into smaller ones

CD1834

Also listen out for signals
that sound different. Those
that come across the
Earth's poles often have a
'watery' or 'fluttery' sound
to them. It is also possible to pick up some interesting stations as the band is closing at night. At this time interference
levels may be less from short-skip stations and competition
from stations to the east will also be less. Also, under these
conditions long-distance stations are often heard.

**Fig 7.3. The
locator system**

These and many other techniques will be learned quickly
and all help the DXer to be able to make more successful
contacts with rare and interesting stations.

## Locators

One feature of VHF and UHF operation is the practice of using
a locator system. Essentially this enables stations to give their
locations fairly accurately without having to resort to latitude and longitude.

The one approved by the International Amateur Radio
Union (IARU) is called the *IARU Locator system*. It splits the
world up into a matrix of main squares which occupy 20°
latitude by 10° longitude. These squares are designated by
two letters. The first refers to the longitude and the second
the latitude, starting at 180° west and 90° south with the
square 'AA' and finishing at 180° east and 90° north with
'RR'. They are the first two characters ('IO') in Fig 7.3.

These squares are each subdivided into a hundred smaller
squares occupying 2° of longitude and 1° of latitude. These
squares are given numeric designations starting with '00' in
the south west and '99' in the north east. These two numbers
occupy positions 3 and 4 in the locator ('91' in our example).

A final subdivision is made to enable the location to be
fixed even more precisely. These areas are designated by
letters starting with 'AA' and finishing with 'XX', and they
occupy the last two positions in the locator. The size of these

**Fig 7.4. A locator map of Europe, showing the large and medium-sized 'squares' corresponding to the first four characters of the locator**

last areas is 5' longitude by 2.5' latitude. These are the letters 'SK' in the example shown in Fig 7.3.

Fig 7.4 shows a locator map of Europe.

## QSL card collecting

When a contact has been made it is often nice to have it confirmed with a *QSL card*. These cards, deriving their name from the Q-code meaning "I confirm reception", are usually postcard sized. They contain the essential details of the

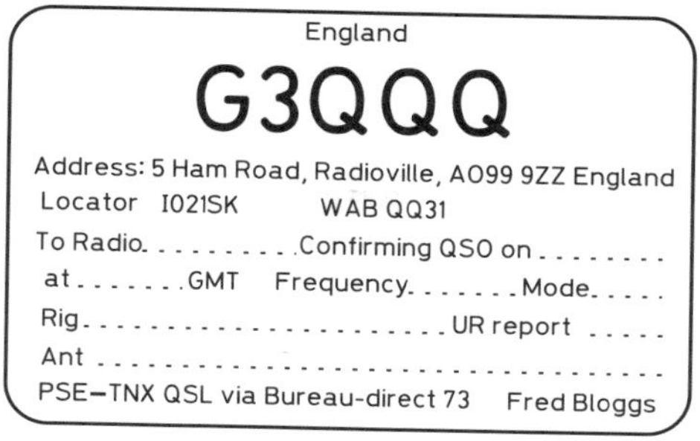

contact and are often very colourful, sometimes with photographs
on the front. Although there is no
hard and fast rule about how a card
should look or exactly how the
information should be presented,
it should contain certain details
about the contact.

Firstly the card has the callsign
of the station printed prominently

England

# G3QQQ

Address: 5 Ham Road, Radioville, AO99 9ZZ England
Locator  IO21SK        WAB QQ31
To Radio. . . . . . . . . .Confirming QSO on . . . . . . . .
at . . . . . . .GMT   Frequency. . . . . . .Mode. . . . .
Rig. . . . . . . . . . . . . . . . . . . . . .UR report  . . . . .
Ant . . . . . . . . . . . . . . . . . . . . . . . . . . . . . . . . . . .
PSE—TNX QSL via Bureau-direct 73   Fred Bloggs

Fig 7.5. A typical
QSL card

on it, together with its address or location and the name of
its owner. Obviously the callsign of the station with whom
the contact was made is needed, along with the date and
time (usually in GMT or z), the frequency band or frequency
and the mode in use. The report that was given in the contact should be included and details of the equipment are
also very useful. Then there is normally space to say whether
a return QSL card is wanted and the route that can be used;
typically the wording is 'PSE/TNX QSL DIRECT/VIA BURO'.
Finally there is a space for the operator's signature.

Many people enjoy sending and receiving QSL cards and
millions are sent each year. As most of them cross country
borders and many are sent from one continent to another,
the cost of sending them by post can be very large. To help
reduce this a system known as the *QSL Bureau* has been set
up. National radio societies act as a collecting point and stations are able to send their cards there in bulk. The cards are
sorted into countries along with those from other members,
and then can be sent abroad in bulk. They are again sorted
and sent to the destination station, again several at a time.
Although the system does take much longer than sending
them direct, ie via the post, it is very much cheaper and it is
often worth the additional wait.

As some stations in remote areas of the globe may receive
many thousands of cards it may not be convenient or practical for them to handle all the cards themselves. Accordingly
some stations have people who act as QSL managers. Normally the manager will be announced over the air and stations sending them should direct their cards to the manager
and not to the station directly.

A selection of QSL cards from around the world

As many DX stations receive many thousands of cards, those wanting a direct response should include return postage. For stations abroad this can be done using international reply coupons (IRCs). They are quite expensive and often stations will ask for at least two to cover the postage. However, it can sometimes be worthwhile to get the card of a particularly rare station.

# Awards

Another interest that many people have is to work towards gaining some of the hundreds operating awards that are available. These present an interesting challenge, and once they have been gained they look very attractive and can be mounted in picture frames and dis-

played in the radio shack. There are awards for the HF bands and for bands at VHF and above, so whatever your field of interest and class of licence there are awards available.

One of the most famous is the DX Century Club award (DXCC). This is awarded by the American Radio Relay League (the US national amateur radio society) to people who can supply proof (QSL cards) that they have made contact with stations in a hundred countries. For people who have contacted more, there are endorsements that can be added. In fact some people have made contact with over 300 countries, and this represents a considerable achievement.

Another popular award that can be used to start your collection is the Worked All Continents. This is issued by the International Amateur Radio Union (IARU) and can be obtained through the RSGB. It can be gained by submitting proof of making contact with stations in five continents, namely Europe, North America, South America, Asia and Oceania.

For the VHF and UHF operator there are also many awards. As the distances that can be achieved are generally not so great there is less emphasis on making contact with different countries. For example, for the VHF Countries and Postal Districts award the number of countries and postal districts needed depends upon the band used, and on 144MHz nine countries and 65 postal districts are required for the standard award. It is also available to listeners on a 'heard' basis.

Further details of these awards are available in the *RSGB Yearbook* or from the RSGB.

## Contests

At certain times of the year the bands erupt with activity when a contest is on. Contests can be very exciting, and it is possible to contact a large number of stations from many new and interesting areas. For those on the HF bands it can be a time when a large number of new countries may be contacted, and for those on VHF and UHF new locator squares, counties and postal districts.

In most contests the idea is to contact as many other stations as possible during the time of the event. Points may be gained in a number of ways. They may be given for each station contacted (there may be more if they are in another country or continent), and then multipliers may be given for the number of different countries or zones etc contacted. Each contest has its own rules and they differ from one to the next. A summary of the major contests is given in Table 7.2.

## Summary

Whilst there are many types of contact there are a few guidelines that should be followed whatever the frequency band or type of contact. A radio amateur should always be polite and courteous. He/she should be helpful, and be aware of others on the air, remembering not to cause interference or use frequencies others have used first. His/her language should be clean, and subjects like politics and religion should be avoided.

It is well worth remembering to spend plenty of time listening to find out the operating standards first. Also, listen before transmitting and find out if the frequency is in use. Whilst there is always the temptation to press the transmit button, all the best operators agree that time spent listening is very well spent.

Also remember that there are plenty of different types of operating. Some people like DXing, others like chatting to local friends. Other people enjoy using data modes. But whatever your own brand of operating, try to explore new

## Table 7.2. Major amateur radio contests

| Contest | Bands | Date | Comments |
|---|---|---|---|
| ARRL DX Contest (CW) | HF | Third full weekend in February | Stations contact USA/Canada |
| ARRL DX Contest (SSB) | HF | First full weekend in March | Stations contact USA/Canada |
| CQ-Worked PrefiXes (WPX) (SSB) | HF | Last full weekend in March | Stations contact as many stations as possible. Extra points given for new prefixes contacted. |
| CQ-Worked PrefiXes (WPX) (CW) | HF | Last full weekend in May | Stations contact as many other stations as possible. Extra points are given for new prefixes that are contacted. |
| CW Field Day (UK) (CW) | HF | Usually first weekend in June | British portable stations make as many contacts as possible. |
| All Asia (SSB) | HF | Third full weekend in June | Contact stations in Asia. |
| VHF Field Day (SSB / CW) | VHF | First full weekend in July | British portable stations make as many contacts as possible. Operation is mainly SSB. |
| IARU-Radiosport (SSB / CW) | HF | Second full weekend in July | Contact as many stations as possible. Extra points given for new countries contacted. |
| Worked All Europe-DX (CW) | HF | Second full weekend in August | Stations outside Europe contact as many European stations as possible. |
| All Asia (CW) | HF | Last full weekend in August | Contact stations in Asia. |
| SSB Field Day (SSB) | HF | First full weekend in September | Portable stations make as many contacts as possible. |
| RSGB Trophy | VHF | First full weekend in September | Many portable stations set up. Aim of contest is to make as many contacts as possible. |
| Worked All Europe-DX (SSB) | HF | Second full weekend in September | Stations outside Europe to contact as many European stations as possible. |
| CQ-WorldWide (SSB) | HF | Last full weekend in October | Contact as many stations in as many countries as possible. |
| CQ-WorldWide (CW) | HF | Last full weekend in November | Contact as many stations in as many countries as possible. |

avenues of the hobby because there is always something new to do that can be very interesting.

Finally, operating your station is meant to be enjoyable so do enjoy your time on the bands.

## Further information

- Up-to-the-minute information about operating can be found each month in *RadCom*, the magazine of the Radio Society of Great Britain, and on the Internet.
- *RSGB Yearbook*, Mike Dennison (ed), RSGB (published annually).
- *Amateur Radio Operating Manual*, 5th edn, Ray Eckersley (ed), RSGB, 2000.
- *Guide to VHF/UHF Amateur Radio*, Ian Poole, RSGB, 2000.

# CHAPTER 8

# Radios

## *In this chapter:*

- Receiver controls and how to use them
- Types of receiver and how they work
- Performance (sensitivity and selectivity)
- Buying a receiver
- Additional equipment

T HE radio receiver is the most important element in any radio station, be it a listening or transmitting station. Today there is a large variety of radios, from small transistor portable receivers, through scanners and 'world band' radios to professional communications receivers. The cost of these sets varies considerably. A professional communications receiver will cost many times that of an ordinary broadcast portable set. Its performance is also far better, being designed to meet the exacting requirements needed for the discerning user.

## Controls

Each type of receiver is designed for different types of use but whatever type of set is available there is plenty on the bands that can be heard. However, to make the best use of the set it is necessary to know how to use it properly. Fortunately, many of the controls are similar and, once the concept behind each one is grasped, this makes operating almost any receiver very much easier.

### Tuning

Obviously the most important control on any set is the tuning control. Whilst on some sets it may be located almost anywhere on the receiver, on communications receivers it tends to be located near the centre of the front panel. This position is chosen because the receiver is generally situated on a table, and it makes for much easier use over long periods of time. The tuning knob should be able to give sufficient control to tune in the wide variety of signals that may be received. Signals such as single sideband or Morse require fine adjustments to the receiver frequency to be made because small frequency changes can make a significant difference to the signal. Modes such as FM and AM can accommodate much coarser levels of control. Some sets even have variable tune rates that can be programmed in, allowing for a fine tuning resolution where very narrow bandwidths are used and coarser tuning for wide–band modes. This makes tuning over large sections of the spectrum much easier.

The control should be smooth and not have any *backlash*. Unfortunately it is the case that many mechanical tuning

A typical communications receiver

arrangements do have backlash. When the direction of tuning is reversed the 'slack' in the tuning has to be taken up before the frequency of the set itself is changed. This can be quite annoying if it is present to any degree.

## Bandswitch

Some receivers today do not have a bandswitch as they are able to tune continuously from one end of their frequency spectrum to the other. However, other receivers, especially older ones, have a switch for the different bands they cover. The switch is required to change the tuning ranges of the circuits being used for the particular band. A number of older receivers were 'amateur bands only' and the switch would be operated to change from one band to the next. This had the advantage that it was very easy to change bands as one operation only was required.

## Keypad

Today many receivers are controlled by a microprocessor and this gives a considerable amount of additional flexibility to these sets. To communicate with the processor and take advantage of many of these facilities a small keypad is often included as part of the front panel. Not only does this include keys for entry of numerals, but there are also special keys for controlling a number of the functions of the set.

## Memories

One of the functions present on many receivers is a memory. Using this it is possible to store the frequency of a particular

**A typical scanner**

station. As most sets with a memory facility have a hundred or more frequencies that can be stored this means that it is possible to store a great variety of stations. For example it would be possible to store the frequencies of a group of broadcast stations that are being monitored. Often the same station broadcasts on several frequencies and, using the memory facility, it is possible to quickly monitor each one to check for the best reception.

## Scan

Another facility that is present on many modern-day receivers is the ability to scan a band of frequencies. Either the set can be programmed to scan between one frequency and another, or it can be made to scan through the memory channels, automatically stopping when a signal is found. This facility is found in all scanners and it particularly useful when monitoring a variety of channels. Once a signal is found the set will stop whilst the transmission is present, and then continue to scan the remaining channels once the signal disappears. In this way a number of channels can be monitored very easily and the chance of missing a vital transmission is reduced.

## AF/RF gain

An AF gain or volume control is present on virtually every radio, and its operation is very straightforward. It is simply used to set the level of volume required to listen to the set.

Many sets also have an RF gain control. This is used to adjust the gain of early stages of the set. If very strong signals are present then some stages in the receiver may become overloaded. By reducing the level of gain, this can be prevented. Under normal operation most people leave the RF gain set to maximum because the best signal-to-noise ratio is obtained if the gain of the first stages is maximised.

Although not common practice these days, some sets have an IF gain control. This should be used in the same way as the RF gain control, reducing the gain of the RF stages first, then the IF stages.

**An example of a 'world band' receiver**

## Mode switch

There is a variety of modes that can be received: AM, FM, SSB and Morse are the most common. In order to be able to demodulate these different types of modulation, different circuits are required within the receiver. Some receivers, and in particular scanners, may default to a particular type of modulation for a given band but most sets that are intended for use apart from just broadcast listening have a switch so that the correct type of demodulator can be selected. On some sets there may be the option to switch in a beat frequency oscillator (BFO) so that Morse and SSB signals can be received. In these cases the position with the BFO out of circuit is used for AM reception. Also 'world band' receivers with a VHF FM broadcast band will automatically switch to FM for this band.

A little practice is needed to tune in single sideband signals, but after the first few signals have been tuned in it quickly becomes second nature. First set the receiver to either upper sideband (USB) for amateur transmissions above 10MHz or lower sideband (LSB) for amateur transmissions below 10MHz. Then slowly tune the receiver until a single sideband signal is heard. Tune the set slowly until the

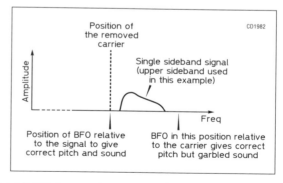

**Fig 8.1. Resolving SSB**

signal is at the correct pitch, and it should then become intelligible. If it does not, then change from USB to LSB or vice versa. For receivers where there is a BFO but no position for USB or LSB, turn the BFO off and then tune in a single sideband signal for maximum strength. Turn the BFO on and adjust it to give the correct audio pitch and intelligibility. It will be found that the BFO can be tuned either side to give the correct pitch, but it will only be intelligible in one position. Once set the pitch control can normally be left in position for the next signal.

### Filter bandwidth

Choosing the correct bandwidth for a particular type of transmission can be very important. Different types of transmission occupy different amounts of bandwidth. Accordingly it is necessary to use the required bandwidth filter for any given type of transmission as described later in this chapter. Often the filters may be labelled for the type of transmission they are intended to receive. This makes it easy to identify the correct filter bandwidth.

### Audio filter

Some receivers will use what is called an *audio filter*. As the name suggests, this is a filter that is placed in the audio stages of the receiver.

These filters generally have two uses. One with a relatively high bandwidth can be used for reception of SSB signals and provides a reduction in the high frequency 'monkey chatter' noise that results from off–channel signals. However, audio filters are more widely used to give a very narrow band filter for use with Morse reception. When used with good filters in the previous stages of the receiver, audio filters can provide a very-cost–effective method of gaining a very narrow bandwidth in the final stages of the set.

### Notch filter

When receiving SSB and Morse, annoying whistles or *heterodynes* may be present. These may be removed by a notch filter which removes a narrow band of frequencies, and may be adjusted in frequency.

## AGC

The strength of signals varies by an enormous amount. From the very weakest to the strongest the difference might be as much as 100 decibels (dB), ie a power ratio of 10,000,000,000 times. This is a vast range, and as a result receivers today have circuitry to adjust the level of gain in the set to accommodate this. The level of the signal is detected and a voltage is fed to the earlier stages so that the gain is reduced as the signals become stronger. The effect of this can be noted particularly well when receiving an AM station on a car radio.

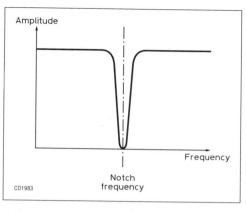

Fig 8.2. The response of a notch filter

As the car moves the signal level varies considerably but the output level will remain almost constant. The main difference that is noticed is that as the signal becomes weaker the level of background noise or interference rises.

In some instances the AGC can be turned off, or the time constant associated with it can be changed. Generally a slow characteristic is required for SSB to enable the syllables of the speech to be accommodated. For Morse a faster AGC characteristic can be tolerated. In most cases, though, an option is not provided and the design of the receiver is optimised for all types of transmission.

### Preselector/RF tuning

Although not particularly common these days, a preselector or RF tuning control may be found on some receivers. Its purpose is to adjust the tuning of the early stage or stages in the receiver so that they are exactly on tune. This is required because loading effects of the antenna, or the way in which they track or follow the tuning of the later stages may vary slightly.

By using this control the wanted signal level can be peaked and any unwanted signals arising from spurious responses in the receiver can be minimised.

# Types of receiver

The primary function of a receiver is to accept incoming signals, select the one on the required frequency, amplify it and then separate the modulation so that the signal can be heard via headphones or loudspeaker, or connected to another unit such as a computer for processing. However, there are a number of ways in which this can be achieved and there are several different types of set. The simplest is a *crystal set* consisting simply of a tuned circuit and diode detector or demodulator. These were some of the first sets that were used, and they can still be built today. *Tuned radio frequency* (TRF) receivers were also widely used – they included an amplifier to increase the signal strength. However, both of these sets lack the selectivity required on today's crowded bands. As a result two other types of receiver are more commonly used. These are the *direct conversion receiver* and the *superhet*.

## Direct conversion

The direct conversion receiver is popular, especially with home constructors. It combines a high level of performance with a relatively straightforward and simple level of construction, although there are a couple of drawbacks that make it unsuitable for general use.

One of the key processes that take place in the direct conversion receiver, and for that matter the superhet, is a process known as *mixing*. This is not the same as audio mixing where two or more audio signals are summed to pass through an amplifier in the most linear fashion as possible to reduce distortion. Instead radio frequency mixing is a non-linear process. Here the two inputs are multiplied together. When this is done, a variety of signals are seen at the output. Not only are there the two original signals but two further signals at frequencies equal to the sum and difference of the input signals. In other words, if signals at 2MHz and 3MHz enter the mixer, then new signals at 3MHz − 2MHz = 1MHz and 3MHz + 2MHz = 5MHz are seen, as shown in Fig 8.3.

The direct conversion receiver uses this process at the core of its operation. Signals enter the mixer from the antenna as shown in Fig 8.4. Here they are mixed with a locally

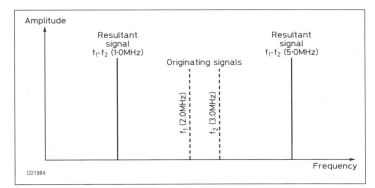

**Fig 8.3. The mixing process**

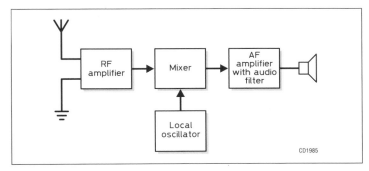

**Fig 8.4. Block diagram of a direct conversion receiver**

generated signal. If the local oscillator is running on a frequency of 1MHz and there is an incoming signal at 1.001MHz, then signals at 0.001MHz or 1kHz and 2.001MHz will be produced. The signal at 2.001MHz is well above the audio range and will not pass through the filter and the audio amplifier. However, the signal at 1kHz will.

Tuning the receiver is then simply a matter of altering the frequency of the local oscillator. By tuning it up or down in frequency, different frequencies will mix with the oscillator and be allowed through the filter and into the audio amplifier. Sometimes radio frequency tuning ahead of the mixer is included. This is simply to prevent signals on all frequencies being presented to the mixer and overloading its input.

The problem with this type of receiver is that the signal being received will create what is known as a *beat note* with the local oscillator. This is fine for Morse signals as this will give the characteristic tone that is turned on and off. It

**99**

also works well with single sideband. However, for AM it is necessary to tune the receiver so that it becomes 'zero beat' with the incoming signal, otherwise an annoying hetero-dyne is heard. It is also not possible to receive FM with this type of receiver.

## Superhet

The superhet is by far the most common type of receiver in use today. From portable broadcast receivers to communica-tions sets, and hand-held walkie-talkies to mobile phones, the superhet is used in all of these applications and many more. It is more complicated than many other types of re-ceiver such as the direct conversion, but it is far more versa-tile and capable of providing excellent results.

Like the direct conversion receiver the superhet uses the mixing process. However, this time the incoming signal is converted down to a fixed intermediate frequency stage where the signal is amplified. Once through this it is de-modulated to regenerate the original audio signal.

A block diagram of a basic superhet radio is shown in Fig 8.5. Here it can be seen that the signal enters the RF amplifier. This stage not only provides some amplification of the signal, but also some tuning. The signal enters the mixer and is mixed with a local oscillator signal. The output is then passed through the intermediate frequency (IF) amplifier and filter. It is in the IF stages where the main filtering occurs and stations on adjacent channels are rejected. It is worth spending a little time looking more closely at the way in which this works. Take the example of a local oscillator running at a frequency of 5MHz. An incoming signal on 5.5MHz will mix with it to produce signals at 10.5MHz and 0.5MHz (ie 5.5 − 5.0MHz and 5.5 + 5.0MHz). If the IF is at a frequency of 0.5MHz then it can be seen that the signal at 5.5MHz will be converted down to 0.5MHz and pass through the amplifier and filter. The signal at 10.5MHz will be ignored. By moving the local oscillator to 6.0MHz it can be seen that a signal at 6.5MHz will produce a signal at the output of the mixer and pass through the amplifier and filter.

The problem with the system is that it is possible for two signals to mix with the local oscillator and produce a signal

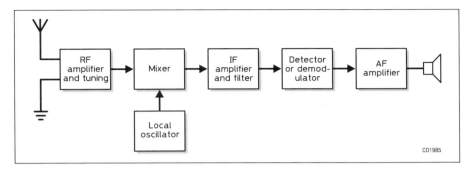

at the intermediate frequency. With the local oscillator set to 5.0MHz we have seen that a signal at 5.5MHz will produce another signal at 0.5MHz after the mixer. However, it is also possible for a signal at 4.5MHz to mix with the local oscillator and give a signal at 0.5MHz. (5.0 – 4.5MHz gives a difference of 0.5MHz.) To prevent this signal from entering the mixer, tuning is incorporated in the radio frequency (RF) amplifier. This tuning does not have to be very sharp because it is only required to remove the unwanted or *image* signal See Fig 8.6.

Once the signal has passed through the IF stages it needs to be demodulated. Different types of demodulator are usually required for different types of modulation. For amplitude modulation a simple *envelope detector* normally consisting of a diode and a few other components is needed. This senses the changes in the amplitude of the signal and converts them into voltage variations that can then be amplified and passed

**Fig 8.5. Block diagram of a basic superhet radio**

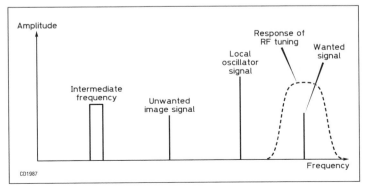

**Fig 8.6. RF tuning removes the image signal**

into the audio amplifier before being converted into sound waves by a loudspeaker or headphones. For single sideband and Morse a BFO and mixer is required. Often the mixer is referred to as a *product detector* in this application.

## Sensitivity

If a receiver is to be able to hear weak signals it must be as sensitive as possible. The actual sensitivity is not limited by the amount of gain that can be achieved. It is possible to obtain very high levels of gain with comparatively little difficulty. Instead the main limiting factor is noise. The receiver may pick this up from the antenna, or it may be generated within the set itself. The received noise arises from a number of sources. It may be atmospheric noise from sources like thunderstorms or it may be galactic, coming from outer space. As the frequencies increase the received noise reduces and eventually a point is reached where the noise generated within the receiver circuitry dominates. As a very broad rule, it is found that on the short-wave bands the received noise dominates, but at VHF and above the noise generated within the receiver becomes the dominant factor.

For receivers on the short-wave bands a measure known as the *signal-to-noise ratio* is generally used. This looks at the level of input signal required to give a signal output compared to the noise output. Normally the signal-to-noise ratio is expressed in decibels (a method of comparing signals on a logarithmic basis). Typically a good short-wave communications receiver might have a sensitivity of 0.25μV for a 10dB signal-to-noise ratio in a 3kHz bandwidth using SSB. The lower the input voltage required to give the 10dB signal-to-noise ratio, the more sensitive it is.

For sets that cover frequencies above 30MHz it is often more normal to quote a specification called a *noise figure*. This is a measure of how much noise a receiver or other item adds. A perfect unit would add no noise at all but this is obviously not possible.

The figure is expressed in decibels. For example, many preamplifiers have a noise figure of 1dB or better. A good receiver might have a noise figure of 4dB or more. General-coverage receivers might easily have a noise figure of 8 to

10dB. The lower the figure, the better the noise performance.

## Selectivity

It is important to ensure that a receiver is able to reject stations on adjacent channels sufficiently well. It is also important to have a variety of different degrees of selectivity in a good receiver because different modes of transmission occupy varying degrees of bandwidth. Accordingly it is important to match the receiver bandwidth to that of the mode of transmission being received. Too wide and the receiver will allow unwanted noise and interference through. Too narrow and the receiver filters will not allow the whole of the transmission through, and this will result in distortion and loss of intelligibility.

Typically for an AM broadcast transmission a bandwidth of 6kHz is considered adequate for the short-wave bands. Around 9kHz may be used for the medium- and long-wave bands where better fidelity is required. For single sideband a figure of 2.5 or 3kHz is generally used and for Morse bandwidths of 500Hz, 250Hz or possibly less can be used, especially when conditions are difficult.

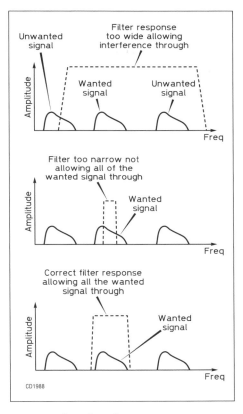

**Fig 8.7. Selecting the correct filter bandwidth**

When specifying filters a variety of figures are used. With an ideal filter the *pass band*, ie the frequency band where signals are allowed through, and the *stop band*, ie the bandwidth for which signals are rejected, is the same. In reality it is not possible to make a perfect filter, although the performance of many filters, and especially crystal filters, is very good. The pass band is defined as the bandwidth where the signal drops by 6dB. The stop band is the bandwidth where the signal level has dropped by 60dB as shown in Fig 8.8. In

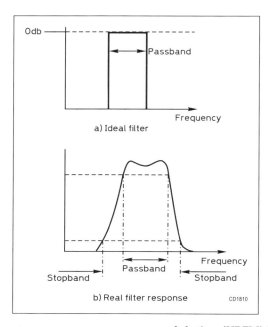

a) Ideal filter

b) Real filter response    CD1810

**Fig 8.8. Ideal and real filters**

some instances the attenuation figures may vary, so it is usual for specifications to be in the form: a bandwidth of 2.7kHz at −6dB and 6kHz at −60dB.

## Modes required

It is important to ensure that the receiver can accommodate the modes that are most likely to be received. In general a receiver for use on the short-wave bands should be able to resolve AM, SSB and Morse (CW). FM is used considerably less on these frequencies, and is really only used for CB and for some amateur transmissions at the top of the 10m band. On frequencies above 30MHz, narrow-band frequency modulation (NBFM) is more widely used, although in the aircraft band above 108MHz amplitude modulation is still used. Also radio amateurs use modes such as SSB and Morse, apart from the variety of data modes.

## Buying a receiver

A receiver will be one of the most expensive and important purchases for the station. Accordingly it is worth spending a little time to make sure that any receiver that is chosen will be suitable for what is required.

One of the first activities is to decide exactly what is wanted. Whilst this may sound a very obvious step, many people only have a vague idea of what they want when they start to buy a set. Especially if it is your first set, it is worth trying to borrow a receiver from a friend to get a feel for what you want. There is no point in spending plenty of hard-earned cash on a receiver only to find that it does not fit the bill after a short while. It is worth considering what type of listening is to be undertaken: short waves only; radio hams or general coverage; scanning VHF and UHF frequencies. It is also worth considering the facilities and general performance that are required. Price is also another important consideration and linked to this is the decision about buying new or second hand.

When buying new first check out all the possible sets that are available. If possible get hold of data sheets to narrow down the choice. When a decision has been made visit the show room of the dealer and ask to use the receiver you are thinking of buying. If possible try to compare different receivers. Take some time to sit down with it and see whether it really meets the requirements. Does it have all the facilities required? Does it cover all the required bands? Finally does it feel right and would you be happy with it?

However, it is worth looking at the second-hand market as well. There are many good bargains to be bought. A set can be bought from either a dealer or a private individual. Obviously a dealer has a reputation to maintain, and the receiver is likely to come with some form of guarantee. This adds to the cost because nothing comes free and the dealer also has to make his profit. Buying from a private individual can produce some excellent bargains, although there is a greater risk. If the person selling the equipment is known to you then so much the better. If not then a little more caution is needed. Many people who buy and sell cars look at the person selling it. The same idea can be used when buying radio equipment. For example if the house is well cared for then the same is likely to be true for the radio. Use these and other pointers to assess whether the person is likely to give you a good deal. If he is then that can give some degree of comfort. However, it is necessary to take a very good look at the receiver. It can help to take a friend along to give a second opinion and, if in doubt, don't buy the set.

Check the receiver over in a systematic fashion. Does it look as though it has been well cared for? Has it been extensively used? If so, items like switches may have worn. If it has been in a smoker's environment then deposits may build up on switches, making them unreliable. Run though all the controls, checking if they operate correctly. Tune the receiver over all the bands. Can signals be heard at the right strength? Check the stability, especially on older receivers. Tune it into a

**An antenna tun-
ing unit**

broadcast station with the BFO switched on. By tuning the set
to zero beat any drift should be quickly noticed. Another
problem encountered on older sets is that the bandswitch
may be very sensitive to any movement, giving a slight
change in frequency if it is touched

It is worth taking time – only make an offer when you feel
perfectly happy that it is in good working order and that it is
the receiver for you.

Whatever option you take up, a good receiver will provide
many hours of pleasure. It is likely that it will still be very
useful when transmitting on the air. Even though most transmitting stations use transceivers, a second receiver is always
very handy.

## Additional equipment for receivers

Apart from the receiver itself there will be other items of
ancillary equipment that can be used to improve the performance of the receiver or provide additional facilities.

One that many people use is an *antenna tuning unit*. When
connected correctly into the antenna system these units enable the best performance to be obtained from the antenna.

Other items can include *decoders* for the wide variety of
data transmissions that can be heard on the bands these days.
Most of the decoders are able to deal with a wide variety of
types of transmission: Morse, packet, Amtor, fax and so forth.
However, before buying one check that it can decode all the

types of signal that you require now and for the future. A little time researching what is available can ensure the best buy is made.

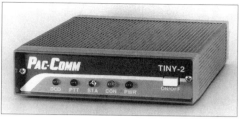

A digital modes adapter (TNC)

For VHF and UHF use *pre-amplifiers* are available. They are most commonly seen for the 2m and 70cm amateur bands where they can provide improved levels of sensitivity. Wide-band preamplifiers are unlikely to give much improvement when used with most sets. They are in fact more likely to cause distortion that would give rise to the presence of unwanted spurious signals.

## Further information

- *Radio Communication Handbook*, 7th edn, Dick Biddulph and Chris Lorek (eds), RSGB, 1999.
- *Superhet Radio Handbook*, Ian Poole, Bernard Babani (Publishing) Ltd.
- *Radio and Electronics Cookbook*, Newnes and RSGB, 2001.
- *Practical Receivers for Beginners*, John Case, RSGB, 1996.

# Antennas

**In this chapter:**

A N ANTENNA (aerial) is an essential part of any radio station. Its performance will have a major influence on the operation of the entire station. A good antenna will make the most of the equipment, whereas a poor antenna will limit the performance of the equipment, however good it is. As a result time and energy invested in improving the antenna system is well spent. In fact experimenting with antennas is an enjoyable activity that can pay major dividends in terms of the performance of the whole station.

## What is an antenna?

An antenna is an element that picks up electromagnetic waves in the form of radio signals from the ether, enabling them to be passed into a receiver as high-frequency electrical signals. Conversely, when power from a transmitter is applied to an antenna this energy is converted into electromagnetic signals that are radiated.

This essentially makes the antenna the 'eyes' of the radio system. Using this analogy it is easy to imagine that the better placed the antenna system is, the better it will be able to 'see' or pick up the signals. Similarly, it will be able to transmit them better as well. Using another analogy, if a light is high up and has a better view of the surrounding area, the light can be seen more clearly further away. A well-placed antenna will be able to radiate its signal better if it is high up and in the open.

## An antenna system

An antenna system consists of three main parts. The first is obviously the antenna element itself. The second is the feeder, and the third is the matching arrangement.

The purpose of the antenna element has already been described. It is the part of the system that is in general thought of as the antenna itself.

However, the feeder is also very important. It enables the signal to be carried from the antenna to the receiver, or conversely from the transmitter up to the antenna. It is important that it introduces as little loss as possible because any loss in the feeder will degrade the performance of the whole system. As a result many people invest in expensive feeder to ensure that the minimum amount of power is lost.

Another requirement of a feeder is that it should not radiate or pick up signals. Not only will this incur power loss, but may also mean that interference is picked up if, for example, the feeder passes through a house where there could be plenty of interference generated. Also, when used with a transmitter, power radiated from the feeder may cause interference to other users if it passes by another receiver that may be affected by the strong signal that could be radiated.

Finally the matching system is required. Both feeders and antennas have an impedance. To ensure that the maximum amount of power is transferred from one to the other, both impedances must be matched. This is achieved by using a *matching unit*. Often these may be referred to as an *antenna tuning unit* (ATU) or sometimes an *antenna matching unit* (AMU).

A large HF and VHF antenna installation

## Feeders

There is a variety of types of feeder that can be used. Coaxial feeder ('coax') is the most widely used, whilst open wire or twin feeder is used in some applications, especially for HF work.

Coaxial feeder consists of two concentric conductors. The inner conductor may be a single conductor or it may be made up of several strands. An insulating dielectric separates the two conductors. Usually this is a plastic material and is often in the form of foam, or it may have several tubes running along it. This is called *semi-air spaced feeder* and, being air spaced, it gives a lower level of loss. The outer conductor is normally in the form of a braid. Covering the braid there is

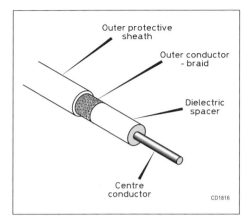

Fig 9.1. Coaxial feeder

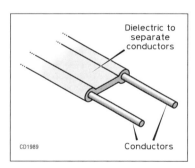

Fig 9.2. Twin feeder

an outer sheath. This provides protection for the feeder and prevents moisture ingress that would introduce loss.

Having a concentric construction means that the inner conductor is fully screened by the outer one and the signal being carried by the feeder is totally enclosed within the outer braid so little of it escapes. It also means that the feeder is not affected by nearby objects and can easily be run through a house.

Most coaxial feeder has a characteristic impedance of either 50 or 75 ohms. 75-ohm feeder is used for domestic applications such as television and hi-fi radio, whereas 50-ohm feeder is used for commercial applications, radio amateurs and CB.

Open wire or twin feeder is used less frequently but nevertheless is still very useful. It consists of two conductors running parallel to each other. As the currents flowing in each of the wires are equal and opposite the resulting fields around the wires cancel each other out and no signal is radiated.

Open wire feeder can be made in a number of ways. It is available commercially made but it is possible to make it yourself. The commercially made varieties come in two main forms but essentially consist of two wires spaced about 1.5cm apart with an insulating dielectric between them to keep the spacing constant (Fig 9.2).

There is the white opaque variety that is used, amongst other things, for making temporary VHF broadcast antennas. This is only suitable for internal use because the plastic absorbs moisture and when this occurs the losses rise. However, there is another type. This uses a black plastic with holes cut in the spacing dielectric. Not only does this reduce the losses but the plastic does not absorb water.

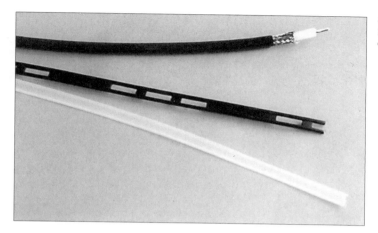

Coaxial cable, black twin and ordinary twin

## Polarisation

It is found that light waves can be polarised. This can be illustrated very easily with a pair of Polaroid® sunglasses. Only when light is polarised in the right direction can the light pass through the Polaroid material. Radio waves can also be polarised and antennas will receive signals with a particular polarisation. A vertical antenna will receive vertically polarised signals and similarly a horizontally polarised antenna will receive horizontally polarised signals. Where signals travel directly between one antenna and another it is important to ensure that the antenna polarisations are the same. If they are different then the signal levels will be reduced.

On the HF bands the antenna polarisation is not particularly critical. Once a signal has been reflected by the ionosphere it has both horizontal and vertically polarised components. Accordingly it is possible to use an antenna with either polarisation, the main requirements being the type of antenna that best fits the location. At VHF and UHF vertically polarised antennas are used universally for FM operation, and horizontal for DX work on SSB and Morse

## Basic long wire antenna

One of the most popular antennas for use on the HF bands is the *long wire antenna*. Although it should more exactly be called an *end-fed wire*, it is nevertheless a very useful and

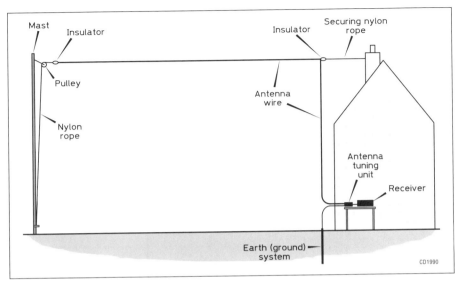

**Fig 9.3. A typical end-fed wire installation**

versatile antenna. For receiving this should be as reasonably long and as high as possible, although especially when transmitting specific lengths are often useful. In these cases it should be an odd number of quarter-wavelengths long.

A long wire can be installed as shown in Fig 9.3, although almost any configuration can be used. It will be seen that insulators are used at the ends of the wire. These can be simple 'egg' insulators like those shown in the diagram. The full ribbed varieties are not really required. Polypropylene rope can be used to secure the insulators to the house and a suitable pole at the remote end. The down lead can then be brought into the shack.

A good earth is needed if a long wire is to be used successfully. Obviously, the mains earth can be used but this is likely to introduce high levels of noise. It is better to use a proper earth for the antenna as described later in the chapter.

Trees provide a convenient high structure that can be used to secure the remote end of an antenna. However, they do move in the wind and if this is not taken into account the antenna will suffer when the wind rises. This problem can be overcome by using a simple system like that shown in Fig 9.4. The loop should contain sufficient slack to enable the

**114**

full movement of the tree under the worst conditions. It should not be so long that it becomes tangled easily.

Whilst long wires are very easy and convenient to install they have some disadvantages. They require the use of an antenna matching unit, especially if they are to be used for transmitting. They also radiate or pick up signals immediately they leave the antenna tuning unit.

This means that when they are used for transmitting there can be high levels of radio frequency power in the shack or radio room. The high RF levels can cause some equipment malfunctions. When used for receiving it means that the antenna is likely to pick up interference from domestic appliances, and the general noise level might be high when compared to other types of antenna that use coaxial or other types of feeder and are located away from the house.

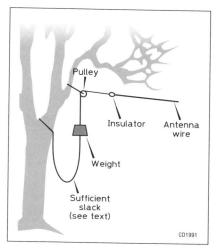

**Fig 9.4. System for attaching a wire antenna to a tree**

## Dipoles

A dipole is one of the most commonly used forms of antenna, forming the basic element of a number of types of antenna as well as being widely used in its own right. In its basic form it consists of a length of wire a half-wavelength long, cut in the middle to allow the feeder to be connected.

**Fig 9.5. A dipole antenna**

As the antenna must be a particular length, it only has a narrow bandwidth over which it can operate efficiently. Typically it will operate satisfactorily over a single amateur band but not very well outside it.

The actual length is slightly shorter than the half-wavelength in free space.

The total length of the antenna can be determined quite easily from the formula:

Length (m) = 148/Frequency (MHz)

Even though this is a relatively good guide

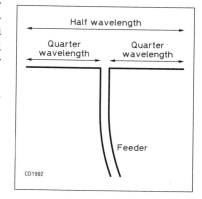

**115**

| Table 9.1. Approximate lengths for half-wave dipole antennas | |
|---|---|
| Frequency (MHz) | Length (m) |
| 1.8 | 82 |
| 3.5 | 42 |
| 7.0 | 21 |
| 10.1 | 14.6 |
| 14.0 | 10.6 |
| 18.0 | 8.2 |
| 21.0 | 7.1 |
| 24.8 | 6.0 |
| 28.0 | 5.3 |
| 50 | 3.0 |
| 144 | 1.0 |
| 430 | 0.34 |

to the length of the antenna it is always good practice to cut the wire slightly longer than is needed and trim it to give the best performance. It is always easier to cut a little wire off than replace wire that has already been removed. A number of factors will affect the performance of the antenna, including the proximity of nearby objects.

Although a dipole is often thought of as a half-wave antenna, it is equally acceptable to have a dipole that is three, five or in fact any odd multiple of half-wavelengths long. This means that an antenna cut for operation on 7MHz can equally be used for operation on 21MHz. This makes the antenna useable on more than one band.

Using an antenna on more than one band can be achieved in other ways apart from running it at multiples of the lowest frequency.

One method is to cut several dipoles and run them from the same feeder. This system works quite well provided the wires are separated from one another reasonably well, and this limits the number to about three sets of wires. They also interact with one another slightly, so it is best to adjust the longest one first and then progress to the shortest.

Another alternative is to place tuned circuits or *(traps)* in the antenna so that at certain frequencies sections of it are isolated. When the antenna is operating at the resonant frequency of the trap, the latter acts as a high impedance and isolates the outer part of the antenna, thereby shortening it. When operated at another frequency the signal is able to pass through and the whole of the antenna is used. In this way the antenna has two resonant frequencies.

It is possible to add further traps to increase the number of bands on which the antenna can operate.

Fig 9.6. It is possible to run several dipoles from a single feeder

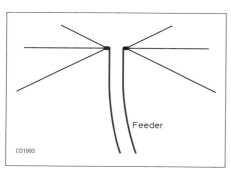

Feeder

CD1993

# Vertical antennas

Horizontal antennas for the HF bands can take up a considerable amount of space, and not every garden is big enough. Vertical antennas can provide the ideal solution in many respects, resulting in a very efficient antenna in a very

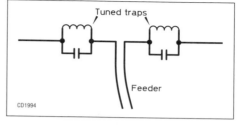

Fig 9.7. A trap dipole

small space. Most verticals are quarter-wavelength and it is either possible to 'ground mount' them, or to use a set of radials (often four) as a *ground plane* against which the antenna can work. When ground mounted the antenna must be at ground level and a good earth connection must be provided for the antenna to work efficiently. When used with a ground plane the antenna can be operated well above ground as the radials simulate the ground. There are generally four, and they are cut to be a quarter-wavelength on the frequency of operation.

In the same way that it is possible to have a trap dipole it is also possible to have a trap vertical. There is a wide variety of commercially made trap verticals. These normally cover a number of the HF bands and are made from aluminium tubing. Wider sections contain the traps for the different bands.

Verticals are also widely used at VHF and UHF, especially on cars because they provide an 'all round' reception and transmission capability, enabling them to function regardless

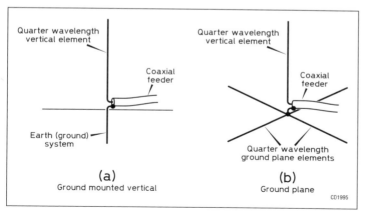

Fig 9.8. Quarter-wave vertical

**(a)** Ground mounted vertical

**(b)** Ground plane

**117**

**Trap vertical**

of the orientation of the car. Other antennas like dipoles are directive and would need to be rotated. Often these antennas are mounted onto cars that they use as a ground plane. Sometimes they are longer than a quarter-wavelength to give improved performance. For base stations, a quarter-wave ground plane with radials may be used but other designs that do not require a ground plane are more commonly used.

## Beam antennas

To improve the performance of an antenna it is possible to beam the power in a particular direction. When transmitting this means that more power is directed where it is wanted and less is wasted by sending it off in directions where it is not needed. Similarly, when receiving these antennas are more sensitive in one direction than the others, reducing the reception of interfering stations.

There are a number of different types of beam but the most popular is called the *Yagi*, named after its inventor, a scientist from Japan. The main element in the antenna is the driven element to which the feeder is connected. This is a dipole. Behind the dipole is an element that is about 5% longer than the dipole or driven element. This is known as the *reflector*, because it reflects signals back to the dipole. In front of the driven element there may be one or more elements that are about 5% smaller than the driven element. These are known as *directors*. Normally only one reflector is ever used, as adding further reflectors behind the first adds little to the performance. However several directors are often used, each one improving the performance slightly.

One of the most common uses for the Yagi is for television reception. Here antennas have eight or more directors.

Radio amateurs use beams on a variety of frequencies. Some HF enthusiasts have arrays that cover three or more bands. Normally the lowest frequency they are used for is 14MHz, although a few beams are used on 7MHz.

At VHF and above Yagis are widely used, especially for DXing. Antennas with eight or eleven elements are common, and for the serious operators antennas with more elements are employed to give the required levels of performance.

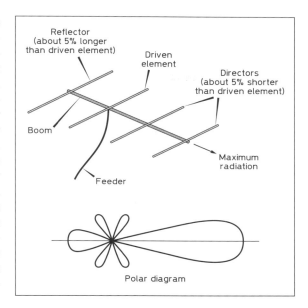

Fig 9.9. A Yagi antenna

When using a directional antenna such as a Yagi, it is necessary to orientate it in the required direction. Normally this is achieved using a motor called a *rotator* that can be controlled from the same location as the receiver or transmitter. A motor on the antenna mast turns the antenna and will only rotate through 360° and then stop. It does not go round more than this otherwise the feeder would become entangled.

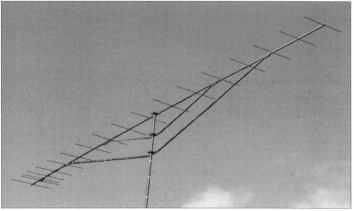

**A Yagi used for the VHF bands**

**119**

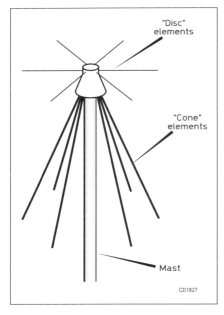

"Disc" elements

"Cone" elements

Mast

CD1827

**Fig 9.10. A discone antenna**

In the radio shack a controller sets the direction of the antenna, and naturally there is an interconnecting cable.

These rotators can be relatively expensive and when installing a beam antenna the cost of the whole system including the antenna, mast, rotator, feeder and so forth should be considered.

## Discone antenna

Most antennas only cover a small band or bands of frequencies. However, when using a scanner receiver it is necessary to have an antenna that covers a much wider range of frequencies. There are a few wide-band antennas and of these the most popular type is called the *discone*. It gains its name from the fact that the elements of the antenna form a disc and a cone as shown in Fig 9.10.

The discone may typically have a frequency range of up to 10 to one, eg it might cover from 100MHz to 1000MHz, although many cover a much smaller range. This antenna is not generally used for transmitting as it is not as efficient as a fully resonant antenna.

## Installation

There are a number of aspects to be thought about when installing an antenna. It is obviously necessary to ensure that it operates optimally, and a little planning before it is erected will enable the choices to be made like the best site and the best way to install it.

Ideally the antenna should be installed as high as possible. In this way it will have the best 'radio view' and it will be able to pick up and radiate signals better. The higher the antenna is placed will mean that the horizon will be further away and this will increase the ranges that can be achieved, especially at VHF and above.

The antenna should also be kept away from objects that

might shield it. It is essential to kept it as far away from any metallic objects as possible. This might include water tanks, wires and many other items. Trees can also have an effect, particularly when they are wet.

It is also an advantage if the antenna can be kept away from the house. Not only can this act as a screen because there are many metallic objects like water tanks and the mains wiring system, it can also be a source of interference, especially on the lower frequencies.

Whilst this is a wish list, any antenna installation will be something of a compromise. Various requirements may have to be traded off against one another to achieve the best overall result. While it is very nice to have an external antenna this is not always possible. Not all is lost if an internal antenna has to be used. The loft or attic is usually the best place, but remember to keep the antenna as far away from the water tank as possible. Also bear in mind that, being inside the house, interference levels will be higher. Not only will this affect the receiver, but when transmitting there is a greater chance of interfering with domestic appliances. Also signal levels will be lower as a result of being inside.

## Safety

One major aspect that must be borne in mind when installing any antenna is that of safety. This is of paramount importance because injuries have resulted either when installing antennas, or if they have fallen down. At all times have an eye open for any problems that might occur. Remember that once an antenna has been exposed to the weather for a while corrosion will occur and winds can be very strong. Only ever use the best components, and make sure they are installed correctly. Under no circumstances should an antenna be able to fall onto a power line. Also take great care when installing the antenna itself. People have been injured and even killed when installing antennas. Make sure that ladders are safe, and that you take precautions when working at any heights. Always make sure that a friend is there in case an accident occurs.

This may sound alarmist but accidents do occasionally occur. By taking precautions it is possible to minimise this possibility so that this fascinating hobby can be enjoyed without the worry of injuries.

## Earth system

An earth system is essential to the operation of many antennas including long (or end-fed) wires and ground-mounted verticals. The ground can conduct electricity, although its resistance is very high. However, as there is plenty of it the resistance between two areas can be very low. The problem is making a good contact to it. There are a number of ways in which this can be done. The easiest is to use an earth stake. This can be obtained from electrical wholesalers and suppliers and consists of a rod driven into the ground. To reduce the resistance further several can be connected in parallel. Alternatively lengths of copper pipe can be buried. Others have used old water tanks. It does not really matter.

Ideally the earth should be as close to the feed point of the antenna as possible. Many of the HF quarter-wave verticals state that the earth connection should be no more than 20 or 30cm from the antenna.

## Further reading

- *Backyard Antennas*, Peter Dodd, RSGB, 2000.
- *HF Antennas for All Locations*, 2nd edn, Les Moxon, RSGB, 1993.
- *Radio Communication Handbook*, 7th edn, Dick Biddulph and Chris Lorek (eds), RSGB, 1999.
- *Practical Antennas for Novices*, John Heys, RSGB, 1994.

CHAPTER **10**

# Setting up the station

*In this chapter:*

- Ideas for locations for the shack
- Installing mains wiring
- Lighting for the shack
- Equipment layout
- Safety in the shack

**M**OST people interested in amateur radio and short-wave listening will want to set up their own station. At first this may only consist of a radio receiver which can be easily placed in a convenient corner. However, as interest grows it is likely that more equipment will be bought, wall maps may be put up and other items required. With this in mind it is convenient to set aside some space for a station or radio shack.

The shack need not be a complete room, although this is ideal. There are many ways of setting aside some space for the radio equipment. A little ingenuity can enable areas of the house that were previously unused to be converted into quite luxurious shacks. To achieve this it is first necessary to look at some of the basic requirements, and then see what areas could be converted.

A variety of areas can be considered: spare rooms, loft spaces or attics, cupboards large and small, spaces in the garage, garden sheds and a whole host more. Each has its own advantages and disadvantages, and by applying a little thought it is often possible to make each one into a good home for the radio equipment.

## Requirements

Before settling on the location of the shack it is worth considering the requirements. For example, some locations may not have easy access for antenna feeders, or mains power may have to be run in specially and these need to be taken into account. Additionally there must be sufficient space. Some shacks tend to grow quite quickly as more equipment is required and all the ancillary items such as components are acquired. On the other hand it may be possible to keep the amount of equipment to a minimum and utilise a much smaller space.

Other considerations include aspects such as noise. The noises emanating from a radio may not be quite as interesting or pleasing to others in the house, and this might mean that it is best to keep it out of the earshot of others. Similarly noises from the rest of the household may distract from listening and result in you not being able to quite hear that weak and interesting DX station. It is also worth bearing in

A well-equipped
radio shack

mind that you may not want the equipment accessible to others, especially if there are small children in the house.

Other aspects like warmth and convenience are also important. It is no fun operating a station when it is very cold or too hot. It takes away much of the real enjoyment and limits the times when the hobby can be enjoyed. The ease with which the station can be accessed may be an issue. It can be very nice to drop into the shack for five minutes to see what conditions are like, or leave the set on so that the bands can be monitored from time to time during the day.

There should also be sufficient room. It should obviously be possible to accommodate all the equipment, and other paraphernalia that is accumulated over the years. There should be sufficient room for a comfortable seat. The hobby is after all a relaxation and a comfortable seat is a definite advantage.

Finally, the table should be deep enough to hold the equipment with several centimetres behind to enable the cables and connectors to be accommodated, remembering that the coax used may not be very flexible. In addition to this there should be sufficient room in front of the equipment to rest your arm. This is particularly important if long periods of operating are envisaged. Typically this might mean that about 35 to 45cm space in front of the equipment is required.

## Possibilities

There are many places that can be considered. A spare room is obviously favourite, as it enables the equipment to be contained within one area, it can be shut off from the rest of the family and there should be sufficient space for the equipment. Mains power and access for the feeders should also not be a problem.

Unfortunately not all of us have this luxury and other options need to be considered. Sometimes this will require a compromise, but some excellent stations have been set up in very restricted spaces.

There is a number of ideas that can be investigated. The first is the loft or attic. In many houses there is a large amount of space in the loft and many people have set their stations up here. One of the main disadvantages of this idea is that a loft gets very hot in summer and cold in winter. Also care must be taken to ensure that the timbers in the loft are not overloaded and that, if alterations need to be made, any building precautions are observed.

An external shed is another option. Whilst many garden sheds may be dirty and uninviting, a little work can convert these into very comfortable locations for a shack. Lining the walls and roof can help retain heat for the winter, and there is good access for feeders. Normally running mains power should not be a problem. The main drawback is security because a shed is reasonably easy to break into, and is not part of the main house. This could make it an easy target.

A garage is another consideration. Normally mains power is available, and feeder access may not be a problem. There may also be plenty of space. However, a garage may be cold in winter and other areas of it may impinge on the radio shack.

Some large walk-in cupboards offer a considerable amount of opportunity and can be made into a very attractive and

Sufficient space should be given to be able to locate it conveniently, bearing in mind that modern screens are large and deep. It is necessary to leave sufficient room for the keyboard and to rest your arms when typing.

Also, for those who enjoy construction, a separate area or work surface slightly away from the main station can be an advantage.

A pin board can be mounted on the wall. This can be used for a map. Dependent upon the bands in use and the likely ranges contemplated, the map could be a world map or one covering possibly your own country or continent. QSL cards and awards can also be mounted. Many QSL cards are very colourful and can add colour and interest to the station. Awards are also worth displaying. Often people use proper picture frames for the awards as they will have spent time working towards them. Many people may not want to put pins through the cards. This can be avoided by mounting the QSL cards onto backing cards using photo corners.

## Safety

A major consideration in any station is that of safety. It is obviously impossible to describe all the features that should be employed here, but we will just give a flavour of some of the points that might be noted.

It is worth using a residual current circuit breaker (RCCB) in the mains circuit for the shack. Although these breakers are not a substitute for other safety measures they are able to provide an additional level of protection against electric shock.

Obviously all the mains wiring should be carefully done, observing the required regulations. Do not be tempted to leave earth connections off or take other short-cuts. It should be remembered that others, including children, may enter the shack and may not be aware of the potential dangers. In fact it is best to make the shack as child proof as possible if there is any chance of them entering.

Other precautions include making sure that no hazardous voltages are accessible. Soldering irons should always be kept in a holder, and switched off when others are around or they are not in use.

Overall the main action is to have a general awareness of safety. It is unlikely that an accident will occur, but the small chance can be reduced to the absolute minimum by making sure all the safety precautions are observed and any potential hazards are minimised. In this way the hobby can be enjoyed in a relaxing fashion, knowing that you and any visitors that may enter the shack will not come to any harm.

## Further reading

- *Amateur Radio Operating Manual*, 5th edn, Ray Eckersley (ed), RSGB, 2000.
- *Radio Communication Handbook*, 7th edn, Dick Biddulph and Chris Lorek (eds), RSGB, 1999.
- *Your First Amateur Station*, Colin Redwood, RSGB, 1997.

# CHAPTER 11

# Constructing your own equipment

*In this chapter:*

- The advantages of constructing equipment
- Kits or building from scratch
- Equipment and tools needed
- Soldering
- Building a small project

HERE is an enormous sense of achievement when a piece of equipment you have built works. This is particularly true when a new homebuilt transmitter is first put on the air and a station comes back to a call. Then with great pride you can say that YOU built it.

Today the need for construction is much less than it used to be. In the very early days of amateur radio there was no commercially made equipment but in recent years considerably more has been available. It is also becoming more difficult for homebuilt equipment to compete in terms of price and performance with the highly sophisticated equipment that be bought from the amateur radio dealers or on the second-hand market.

Yet despite this many people enjoy building their own equipment. Most of it does not have nearly the same complexity and the same number of facilities as that which can be bought, but it is still possible to use it and gain some very good results. In fact some people take pride in the fact that they use only homebuilt equipment and they manage to obtain some excellent results from it. It brings a new dimension to the hobby.

**A typical kit receiver**

## Options available

Several options are open to people wanting to build equipment. The first step is to choose a project that you have a chance of completing. Many people start projects that are never completed. Actually completing gives a tremendous sense of achievement and an incentive to start another item that may be slightly more advanced.

The equipment need not be a transmitter or receiver; it could be a piece of ancillary equipment – possibly an antenna tuning unit. However, simple Morse transmitters can be quite easy to put together and can be fun to set up and test.

**A selection of tools**

The project can be undertaken in a number of ways. Possibly the easiest and most attractive option for many is to build a kit. There are several companies that advertise a good selection of kits for everything from an antenna tuning unit up to transmitters and receivers. In many cases the metalwork can also be bought, enabling the whole job to have a very professional looking finish.

The amateur radio and electronics magazines also publish a number of projects. These are normally more challenging because the whole project has to be assembled from scratch, assuming a kit is not available. However, they can provide some very good experience, although be careful not to start with a project that is too large.

## Equipment

In any amateur radio station, be it for listening or transmitting, a certain number of tools will be required. A good selection of screwdrivers, spanners and the like are very useful. In addition to this a good pair of thin-nosed pliers and wire cutters are essential. It is worth buying reasonable-quality tools. The very cheap ones will not last as long and may damage the screws, nut and bolts etc, causing more work.

A soldering iron is also needed. Even if little construction is envisaged, one will come in useful for making interconnection leads and setting up and keeping the station running.

Generally a 15-watt iron is suitable for most applications, although for items that are larger and absorb more heat a 25-watt iron comes in useful. Normally it is not necessary to spend a lot of money on a soldering iron, but if a really good item is required then the thermostatically controlled versions are very nice. Most irons these days come with a stand. This is essential because the tips become very hot and will cause a burn if touched.

Another useful item for anyone contemplating using a soldering iron is a solder sucker. This can be used to remove the solder from joints and is almost essential when dismantling something or remaking a joint. Although it is possible to survive without one, it is an extremely useful item to have and can make some jobs very much easier.

## Soldering

Soldering is at the very heart of electronic construction and whether used for amateur radio construction or in professional electronic equipment it is equally important. Fortunately it is a skill that is learned relatively easily. One of the main requirements is that the job should not be rushed and it should be done carefully. Then with a little practice the standard of construction can be very high.

When making a joint, the first requirement is that both surfaces should be clean and free from any oxidation. The iron should be at its operating temperature and the bit should be *tinned*, ie have a thin layer of solder applied to it. Both wires or surfaces should also be tinned so they can be soldered more easily. This will help remove any grease and dirt so that a good joint can be made. In fact most leaded components are pre-tinned to help in the soldering process and tinning may not be required.

Both surfaces to be soldered should be brought together. This may entail mounting a component on a printed circuit board, twisting two wires together or possibly inserting wires into a connector for assembly. Once this is done the iron should be brought to the joint, and solder applied to the joint itself. Note that the solder should not be applied to the soldering iron first.

The best joints are made if they are done reasonably quickly. If the solder is kept very hot by the iron for too long then the flux will be used up, allowing oxidation. This will lead to what is known as a *dry joint*. These look frosted and do not have the shiny appearance of a good joint. Dry joints can be very troublesome, giving a poor connection that may be intermittent.

**Fig 11.1. A soldered joint on a printed circuit board**

The amount of solder used to make a joint should be carefully regulated. Enough should be used for it to flow round the joint, but it should not form a large blob over it. With a little practice it soon becomes obvious how much to use.

After the iron has been used for a few joints it will become blackened with the spent flux. This should be removed periodically by wiping the bit on a small damp sponge or cloth. These are normally supplied with the soldering iron stand and should be dampened from time to time. Keeping the bit clean will help ensure that the solder flows easily over the soldering iron and good joints are made.

**A carefully constructed piece of equipment**

A well-constructed piece of equipment can look very pleasing when complete. A well thought-out project that has been carefully made is far more likely to work than one that has been quickly put together. It will also give more pleasure and can be shown to others with pride.

## Beat frequency oscillator project

Many domestic receivers can receive signals on the short-wave bands. However, many do not have a beat frequency oscillator (BFO) and as a result they cannot properly resolve Morse and single sideband signals. Fortunately it is relatively easy to build a small BFO using a handful of components. The project on this page will work with receivers having an intermediate frequency (IF) of between 450 and 470kHz. This IF is used by most receivers. The BFO can sit close to the receiver and not require any direct connections for it to operate satisfactorily, making it an ideal first project.

The BFO can be made on a small piece of matrix board. This is board with a matrix of holes normally spaced 0.1in apart. Components can be mounted on the board with their leads routed through the holes to keep them in place. Alternatively, special pins can be mounted into the holes and components soldered to them. Once built, the BFO can be housed in a plastic box to protect the circuitry and keep it looking tidy. A metal box must not be used because this would screen the signal from the radio and prevent the BFO working.

The circuit diagram is shown in Fig 11.2. From this it can be seen that it uses a single transistor and a few other components. A layout is shown in Fig 11.3. However, before

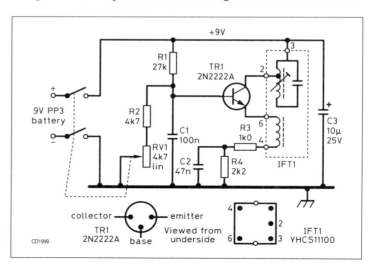

**Fig 11.2. Circuit diagram of the BFO**

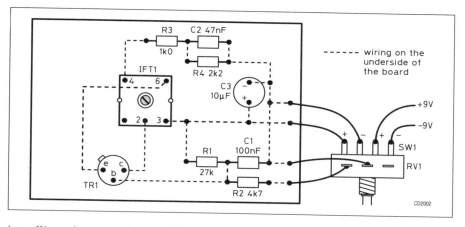

**Fig 11.3. Matrix board layout – component side shown**

installing the transformer IFT1 the metal can should be removed to expose the transformer itself. This will help the signal to radiate and be picked up by the receiver a short distance away. Once this is done the components can be installed and carefully soldered, making sure that each joint is satisfactory. Underneath the board the components can be linked using connecting wire. This should be insulated wire, and each end can be stripped to leave a short length of conductor for soldering. Care should be taken not to leave the soldering iron too long on any of the components and especially the transistor, otherwise damage may result. Also

## Table 11.1. BFO components list

| | |
|---|---|
| R1 | 27k 0.25 watt resistor |
| R2 | 4k7 0.25 watt resistor |
| R3 | 1k 0.25 watt resistor |
| R4 | 2k2 0.25 watt resistor |
| RV1 | 4k7 linear variable resistor (potentiometer) with switch |
| C1 | 100nF ceramic capacitor |
| C2 | 47nF ceramic capacitor |
| C3 | 10µF electrolytic capacitor (radial type) |
| TR1 | 2N222A transistor |
| IFT1 | Toko YHCS11100 intermediate frequency transformer |

Plastic box, approx 100 × 70 × 45mm
Matrix board, approx 80 × 50mm (to fit box)
Battery connector for PP3 battery
Control knob

make sure that C3 is connected the right way round, and that the connections of the transistor are correct.

The leads to the variable resistor/switch (RV1) and the 9V battery should be about 10cm long. Connect these before fitting RV1 into the case so that the circuit can be adjusted before fitting it into the case.

Once a final check has been done to ensure that all the components have been connected correctly and that all the wiring is correct, connect the battery. The assembly should be placed close to the radio it is to be used with. This can be set to an amateur band and then carefully tuned until a single sideband signal is heard. Then turn on the BFO and set the variable resistor to the mid position. Slowly adjust the ferrite core with a small screwdriver, or better still a plastic trimmer tool. Be careful with the core because it is fragile and can break. This should be adjusted until the speech starts to become intelligible. Once set to the optimum position the core should be left and any further adjustments made with the potentiometer.

With the BFO working, it is worth experimenting with the best position for it. The assembly can be mounted in the plastic box. A 10.5mm hole can be drilled for the potentiometer RV1 and matrix board can be mounted on pillars to neatly secure it. Finally screw the base on the box and the unit is completely ready for use. However, remember to turn the BFO off when the radio is turned off.

## Further information

- *Radio and Electronics Cookbook*, Newnes and RSGB, 2001.
- *Practical Wireless* magazine.

# CHAPTER 12

# Getting your own licence

*In this chapter read about:*

- How to obtain an amateur transmitting licence
- The different licences available in the UK
- How to obtain a UK Novice Licence
- How to pass the Radio Amateurs Examination
- How to learn the Morse code

ONCE you have spent some time listening on the bands it is likely that you will want to be able to transmit. This opens a whole new field of amateur radio, enabling you to make friends all over the world, experiment with equipment, install your own transmitting station and fully participate in the hobby in whatever way you want.

To do this it is necessary to obtain an amateur transmitting licence. However, international law requires countries not to issue licences without the applicants proving that they are able to install, maintain and operate their equipment properly. Someone who did not have the relevant knowledge could cause considerable amounts of interference to others worldwide. Fortunately it is not difficult to obtain a licence, and gaining one gives a real feeling of achievement, apart from the fact that you will know more about radio and its technology.

Different countries have different requirements but international agreements require holders of licences that allow access to bands above 30MHz to pass a theory test. To obtain a licence that gives access to bands below 30MHz it is currently necessary to pass a Morse test as well. However, it is likely that in the future the requirement for the Morse test may be relaxed.

## UK licences

In the UK there are a number of licences that can be obtained. Each one gives a different level of privileges and requires tests at a different level to be passed.

The entry level is the Novice licence. There are two forms of this licence, namely the Class A and the Class B licence. The Class B Novice licence gives access to the Novice frequency allocations within the amateur bands above 30MHz, whereas the Class A licence gives access to all the Novice bands including those below 30MHz. The permitted power levels are less than those allowed with the more advanced licence classes, although they are still sufficient to enable many interesting contacts to be made.

To obtain the Novice licence it is necessary to take a short course. This course is aimed at the newcomer to amateur radio and aims to teach many of the fundamentals of radio in a stimulating way by actually doing things. Soldering, building a small project, and a variety of other exercises are included. After this the candidate sits the Novice Radio Amateurs Examination (NRAE). This is a straightforward theory test based on what was learnt on the Novice course, covering the basic concepts of radio, operating on the amateur bands, and the licence conditions. With both of these successfully completed a Class B Novice licence can be obtained. To obtain the Class A Novice licence it is necessary to also sit a Morse test, sending and receiving at 5 words per minute.

There are three other classes of licence, namely the Class A, Class B and Class A/B. To gain a Class B licence it is necessary to pass the Radio Amateurs Examination (RAE). This examination is more advanced than the NRAE, and covers basic radio theory as well as the licence conditions. The licence allows access to all the amateur allocations above 30MHz and with the full power limits.

The Class A licence requires a Morse test (sending and receiving at 12 words per minute) to be passed in addition to the RAE, but gives full access to all the allocations above and below 30MHz.

The Class A/B licence is a 'half way house' between the two licences. It requires the applicant to have passed the RAE and a Morse test, sending and receiving at five words per minute. Like the Class B licence it gives full access to the allocations above 30MHz. Below 30MHz access is allowed on all the frequencies, but with a slightly reduced maximum power limit.

## Studying for the Novice licence

It is necessary to attend a Novice course before taking the NRAE. These courses are run by volunteer radio amateurs and organised nationally by the Radio Society of Great Britain. The course, which generally lasts for about 30 hours over a period of 12 weeks, includes a number of small constructional projects as well as topics on basic radio technology. Students are also taught the procedure that will be needed when operating a station once the licence is gained. This course is particularly useful for anyone entering the hobby. Not only is it the first step to gaining a Novice licence, but it is also teaches the essentials that need to be known to set up and operate an amateur radio station. Information about the training course may be obtained from the Radio Society of Great Britain.

Before moving on to take the examination it is necessary to complete the course successfully. Once this is accomplished it will prepare anyone for the examination, which lasts for 75 minutes and comprises 45 multiple choice questions. It is based on the subjects covered in the course and during the examination a copy of the Amateur Radio (Novice) Licence Schedule is available for reference.

The subjects covered in the examination include: receivers and receiving techniques; components, applications and units; measurements; propagation and antennas; transmitters and transmitting techniques; operating techniques; station layout; construction; safety; licensing conditions. The examination is run by the City & Guilds of London Institute from whom copies of the syllabus and sample copies of the examination may be obtained.

## Studying for the RAE

When studying for the RAE there is no requirement to take a particular course, and it is possible to study at home on your own if you prefer. Many radio societies and technical colleges run courses specifically for the RAE. Details of these are published by the Radio Society of Great Britain.

Alternatively there are some correspondence courses that can be undertaken. However, it is also possible to study from books on your own. Whatever route is adopted, the Radio Society of Great Britain produces books to help. The RSGB *Radio Amateurs Examination Manual* has helped many thousands of people gain their licences and it is regularly updated to take account of changes in the syllabus and the licence. Other publications are also available and detailed at the end of this chapter.

In addition to studying the basic syllabus it is also helpful to read around the subject. Magazines including *RadCom* and others with technical and other articles all help to build up the wider picture about the hobby and the technology. Listening on the air also helps in the same way.

Like the Novice Radio Amateurs Examination, the RAE is set and administered by the City & Guilds of London Institute from whom copies of the syllabus and sample papers may be obtained.

## Learning Morse

Many people wonder why they should take Morse these days. Whilst it needs some determination to pass the test, the rewards can be large, apart from just giving access to the HF bands. It is an excellent mode for anyone wanting to make long-distance contacts with a relatively modest station.

There are many ways of learning the code. No one method is the correct one, except to say that the one that works for you is the best. However, there are a few pointers that can help along the way.

The first requirement is determination. Find ways to keep the impetus going. This may be accomplished by going to a course every week, and having to practise between times to keep up. It might be possible to learn with a friend, or someone else may be willing to teach you. By having some reason to keep going it is much harder to give up. If you do it on your own, then set a target you have to meet, otherwise it is very easy to let it slip.

The first stage in learning the code is to learn the sounds of the letters. There are Morse tutor tapes and electronic Morse tutors. By playing the different letters of the alphabet the rhythm of each letter can be learnt. It is no use trying to learn the letter 'A' as 'dot dash' because this does not convey anything of the actual sound that is heard.

Once the sounds for the characters have been learnt it is possible to move on to copying some slow Morse. Again tapes and Morse tutors are useful if a course is not being attended. Here the letters should be sent reasonably fast and a longer gap for thinking left between them. As copying the code becomes more natural the space between them can be reduced.

Initially resist the temptation to send Morse. By sending Morse too early in the learning process, it is very easy to pick up bad habits that are very difficult to 'unlearn' later. However, once up to a reasonable speed it is possible to start sending. Pay particular attention to the sound of the letters being sent. It is even worth recording what is sent and listening to it later.

As experience increases and the speeds that can be copied increase it is possible to start listening on the bands. The bottom of the 80m band has some useful Morse transmissions, especially at the weekends. This can provide some invaluable experience in copying 'live' Morse transmissions. The Radio Society of Great Britain runs a number of slow Morse transmissions. The schedule for these is published in the *RSGB Yearbook*.

It is important to practise regularly. Half an hour a day is far better than three hours at the weekend. If possible try to set aside a certain time for practice each day. By making it a regular time each day it is possible to fit it into the daily routine more easily and not forget it.

With regular practice it is surprising how quickly it is possible to increase your speed. Soon you will be copying signals on the band, some which are reasonably fast. Not only does this prepare you for taking the Morse test, but it also opens the interesting and very useful world of Morse code.

The Morse test is administered by the Radio Society of Great Britain from whom further details may be obtained.

## Applying for the licence

With the courses, examinations and tests complete it is now possible to apply for the licence. Dependent upon the type of licence, the relevant application form should be completed and sent to the Radio Licensing Centre with the required documentation. For a full licence this is the issue fee (if you are under 21 no fee is required); the RAE pass certificate (do not send a photocopy) and for a Class A or A/B licence the Amateur Morse Test pass slip. For a Novice licence the issue fee (if you are under 21 no fee is required) must be included along with the RSGB Novice Licence Training Course Completion Slip; the NRAE pass certificate; and if a Class A Novice licence is required the Amateur Radio Morse Test pass slip.

The application should be posted with the relevant documentation to the address in the appendix to this book. This is processed and in due course the licence will be issued. Then it will be possible to start transmitting on the air.

The first contact is always very memorable, although most people are a little nervous. However, it does not take long to get used to transmitting rather than listening and it is the next stage in appreciating the fascinating hobby of amateur radio. For many people it is a lifelong hobby that they find particularly stimulating and one in which they can make many friends.

Once established there are many different activities that can be tried. Many people enjoy a particular area of amateur radio but it is always worth trying some new avenue. In this way a lively interest can be maintained and a wide variety of activities explored. I have certainly enjoyed the hobby in a variety of areas and benefited greatly from it. I hope you do as well – good luck!

## Further information

- *Radio Amateurs Examination Manual*, John Case and Hilary Claytonsmith, RSGB, 1998.
- *RAE Revision Notes*, George Benbow, RSGB, 1993.
- *Novice Licence Student's Notebook*, John Case, RSGB, 1994.
- *Revision Questions for the Novice RAE*, Esde Tyler, RSGB, 1993.
- *Novice Radio Amateurs Examination Handbook*, Ian Poole, Bernard Babani (Publishing) Ltd.
- *Morse Code for Radio Amateurs*, George Benbow, RSGB, 1993.
- *Instant Morse* (CD-ROM), RSGB.
- Also see the appendix for further contact addresses.

# Sources of information

**General enquiries about amateur radio, amateur radio books, Morse testing, Novice licence courses etc**
Radio Society of Great Britain
Lambda House
Cranborne Road
Potters Bar
EN6 3JE

Tel: 0870 904 7373
Web site: www.rsgb.org

**Information about radio, amateur radio and electronics**
Web site: www.radio-electronics.com

**Address to which licence applications should be sent**
Radio Licensing Centre
The Post Office
PO Box 884
Bristol
BS99 5LF

Tel: 0117 925 8333

**Enquiries about the Radio Amateurs Examination (subject 765), the Novice Radio Amateurs Examination (subject 773)**
City & Guilds of London Institute
1 Giltspur Street
London
EC1A 9DD

Tel: 020 7294 2468

### Information about amateur radio licences, terms conditions etc

Amateur Radio Services
Radiocommunications Agency
Wyndham House
189 Marsh Wall
London
E14 9SX

Tel: 020 7211 0159 / 0160 / 0161 (answerphone)
E-mail: amcb@ra.gtnet.gov.uk
Web site: www.radio.gov.uk

### Information about DX bands and operation, expeditions etc

Web site: www.dxbands.com

### Amateur radio in the USA and the USA national society

American Radio Relay League
225 Main Street
Newington
CT 06111-1494
USA

Web site: www.arrl.org

# Index

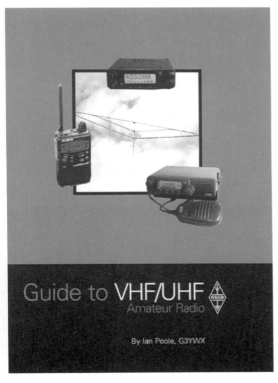

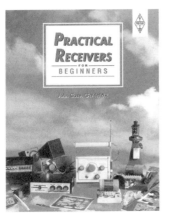

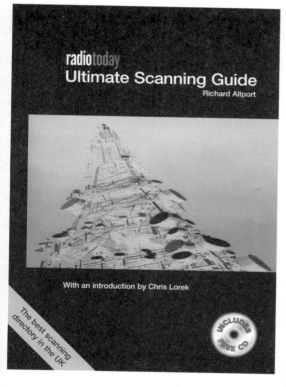

# OTHER RSGB PUBLICATIONS

| Code | Description | Price |
|------|-------------|-------|
| 1-872309-54-2 | Backyard Antennas | £18.99 |
| 1-872309-08-9 | HF Antenna Collection | £9.99 |
| 1-872309-15-1 | HF Antennas for all Locations | £7.99 |
| 1-872309-11-9 | Practical Antennas for Novices | £7.99 |
| 1-872309-36-4 | The Antenna Experimenter's Guide | £17.99 |
| 1-872309-62-3 | The RSGB IOTA Directory 2000 | £9.99 |
| 1-872309-64-X | RSGB Yearbook 2001 Edition | £15.99 |
| 1-872309-48-8 | The RSGB Guide to EMC | £19.99 |
| 1-872309-24-0 | Radio Communication Handbook | £29.99 |
| 1-872309-65-8 | Low Frequency Experimenter's Handbook | £18.99 |
| N/A | Radio & Electronics Cookbook | £16.99 |
| 1-872309-40-2 | PMR Conversion Handbook | £16.99 |
| 1-872309-35-6 | Practical Receivers for Beginners | £14.99 |
| 1-872309-21-6 | Practical Transmitters for Novices | £16.99 |
| 1-872309-30-5. | Radio Data Reference Book | £14.99 |
| 1-872309-61-3 | Technical Topics Scrapbook 1995-99 | £14.99 |
| 1-872309-51-8 | Technical Topics Scrapbook 1990-94 | £13.99 |
| 1-872309-20-8 | Technical Topics Scrapbook 1985-89 | £9.99 |
| 1-872309-23-2 | Test Equipment for the Radio Amateur | £12.99 |
| 1-872309-63-1 | Amateur Radio Operating Manual | £24.99 |
| 1-872309-50-0 | Amateur Radio - the first I 00 years | £49.99 |
| 0-900612-09-6 | World at Their Fingertips | £9.99 |
| 0-90061289-4 | Microwave Handbook Volume 1 | £11.99 |
| 1-872309-01-1 | Microwave Handbook Volume 2 | £18.99 |
| 1-872309-12-7 | Microwave Handbook Volume 3 | £18.99 |
| 1-872309-58-5 | Guide to VHF/UHF Amateur Radio | £8.99 |
| 1-872309-42-9 | The VHF/UHF Handbook | £19.99 |
| 1-872309-26-7 | Morse Code for Radio Amateurs | £4.99 |
| N/A | Prefix Guide (fifth edition, 1999) | £8.99 |
| 1-872309-43-7 | Your First Amateur Station | £7.99 |
| 1-872309-00-3 | G-QRP Circuit Handbook | £9.99 |
| 1-872309-31-3 | Packet Radio Primer | £9.99 |
| 1-872309-38-0 | Your First Packet Station | £7.99 |
| 1-872309-60-7 | Radio Today Ultimate Scanning Guide | £19.99 |
| 1-872309-49-6 | Your Guide to Propagation | £9.99 |
| 1-872309-27-5 | Novice Licence - Student's Notebook | £4.99 |
| 1-872309-28-3 | Novice Licence-Manual For Instructors | £9.99 |
| 1-872309-45- | Radio Amateur's Examination Manual | £14.99 |
| 1-872309-18-6 | RAE Revision Notes | £5.00 |
| 1-872309-19-4 | Revision Questions for the Novice RAE | £5.99 |

# www.rsgb.org/shop
## or Tel: 0870 904 7373

(All prices subject to change without prior notice)